NATIVE AMERICAN VETERANS' ACCESS TO HEALTH CARE

AN EXAMINATION

MILITARY AND VETERAN ISSUES

Additional books in this series can be found on Nova's website
under the Series tab.

Additional e-books in this series can be found on Nova's website
under the e-book tab.

NATIVE AMERICAN VETERANS' ACCESS TO HEALTH CARE

AN EXAMINATION

LORRIE HOBBS
EDITOR

New York

NOTICE TO THE READER

The Publisher has taken reasonable care in the preparation of this book, but makes no expressed or implied warranty of any kind and assumes no responsibility for any errors or omissions. No liability is assumed for incidental or consequential damages in connection with or arising out of information contained in this book. The Publisher shall not be liable for any special, consequential, or exemplary damages resulting, in whole or in part, from the readers' use of, or reliance upon, this material. Any parts of this book based on government reports are so indicated and copyright is claimed for those parts to the extent applicable to compilations of such works.

Independent verification should be sought for any data, advice or recommendations contained in this book. In addition, no responsibility is assumed by the publisher for any injury and/or damage to persons or property arising from any methods, products, instructions, ideas or otherwise contained in this publication.

This publication is designed to provide accurate and authoritative information with regard to the subject matter covered herein. It is sold with the clear understanding that the Publisher is not engaged in rendering legal or any other professional services. If legal or any other expert assistance is required, the services of a competent person should be sought. FROM A DECLARATION OF PARTICIPANTS JOINTLY ADOPTED BY A COMMITTEE OF THE AMERICAN BAR ASSOCIATION AND A COMMITTEE OF PUBLISHERS.

Additional color graphics may be available in the e-book version of this book.

Library of Congress Cataloging-in-Publication Data

ISBN: 978-1-63463-064-1

Published by Nova Science Publishers, Inc. † New York

CONTENTS

PREFACE

The Department of Veterans Affairs (VA) and the Indian Health Service (IHS) have developed mechanisms to implement and monitor their memorandum of understanding (MOU); however, the performance metrics developed to assess its implementation do not adequately measure progress made toward its goals. VA and IHS have defined common goals for implementing the MOU and developed strategies to achieve them. Native Americans who have served in the military may be eligible for health care services from both VA and IHS. This book examines the extent to which the agencies have established mechanisms through which the MOU can be implemented and monitored; and key challenges the agencies face in implementing the MOU and the progress made in overcoming them.

Chapter 1 - Native Americans who have served in the military may be eligible for health care services from both VA and IHS. To enhance health care access and the quality of care provided to Native American veterans, in 2010, these two agencies renewed and revised an Memorandum of Understanding (MOU) designed to improve their coordination and resource sharing related to serving these veterans. GAO was asked to examine how the agencies have implemented the memorandum of understanding (MOU).

This report examines: (1) the extent to which the agencies have established mechanisms through which the Memorandum of Understanding (MOU) can be implemented and monitored; and (2) key challenges the agencies face in implementing the MOU and the progress made in overcoming them. To conduct this work, GAO interviewed VA and IHS officials and reviewed agency documents and reports. GAO also obtained perspectives of tribal communities through attendance at two tribal conferences; interviews with tribal leaders and other tribal members, including veterans; and interviews with other stakeholders, such as health policy experts and consultants.

Chapter 2 - Native Americans who have served in the military may be eligible for health care services from both VA and IHS, but according to reports some have had problems accessing care. In 2010 these two agencies expanded upon an Memorandum of Understanding (MOU) designed to improve Native American veterans' access to care at their facilities. GAO was asked to examine how the Memorandum of Understanding (MOU) has increased access to care.

This report examines: (1) the actions that VA and IHS have taken to implement the provisions in the 2010 Memorandum of Understanding (MOU) related to access to care for Native American veterans, and (2) what is known about how access to care for Native American veterans has improved. To conduct this work, GAO reviewed agency documents and VA and IHS reimbursement data and interviewed VA and IHS officials. GAO also visited three sites selected to reflect geographic variation to learn about access to care locally through interviews with regional VA and IHS officials, health facility officials, and Native American veterans and their tribal representatives. GAO also contacted other individuals who help Native American veterans seek enrollment in the VA to obtain their insights about improvements in access to care.

Chapter 3 - The purpose of this Memorandum of Understanding (MOU) is to establish coordination, collaboration, and resource-sharing between the Department of Veterans Affairs (VA) and Indian Health Service (HIS) to improve the health status of American Indian and Alaska Native Veterans. The goal of the MOU is to foster an environment that brings together the strengths and expertise of each organization to actively improve the care and services provided by both.

The MOU establishes mutual goals and objectives for ongoing collaboration between VA and IHS in support of their respective missions and to establish a common mission of serving our nation's American Indian (AI) and Alaska Native (AN) Veteran. The MOU is intended to provide authority for a broad range of collaboration between the agencies that facilitate development of additional agreements around specific activities. It is the intent of this MOU to facilitate collaboration between IHS and VA, and not limit initiatives, projects, or interactions between the agencies in any way.

The MOU recognizes the importance of a coordinated and cohesive effort on a national scope, while also acknowledging that the implementation of such efforts requires local adaptation to meet the needs of individual tribes, villages, islands, and communities, as well as local VA. IHS, Tribal, and Urban Indian health programs.

In: Native American Veterans' Access ...   ISBN: 978-1-63463-064-1
Editor: Lorrie Hobbs   © 2014 Nova Science Publishers, Inc.

Chapter 1

VA AND IHS: FURTHER ACTION NEEDED TO COLLABORATE ON PROVIDING HEALTH CARE TO NATIVE AMERICAN VETERANS[*]

United States Government Accountability Office

WHY GAO DID THIS STUDY

Native Americans who have served in the military may be eligible for health care services from both VA and IHS. To enhance health care access and the quality of care provided to Native American veterans, in 2010, these two agencies renewed and revised an MOU designed to improve their coordination and resource sharing related to serving these veterans. GAO was asked to examine how the agencies have implemented the MOU.

This report examines: (1) the extent to which the agencies have established mechanisms through which the MOU can be implemented and monitored; and (2) key challenges the agencies face in implementing the MOU and the progress made in overcoming them. To conduct this work, GAO interviewed VA and IHS officials and reviewed agency documents and reports. GAO also obtained perspectives of tribal communities through attendance at two tribal conferences; interviews with tribal leaders and other

---

[*] This is an edited, reformatted and augmented version of the Highlights of GAO-13-354, a report to congressional requesters, dated April, 2013.

tribal members, including veterans; and interviews with other stakeholders, such as health policy experts and consultants.

WHAT GAO RECOMMENDS

GAO recommends that the agencies take steps to improve the performance metrics used to assess MOU implementation and to develop better processes to consult with tribes. VA and the Department of Health and Human Services agreed with these recommendations.

WHAT GAO FOUND

The Department of Veterans Affairs (VA) and the Indian Health Service (IHS) have developed mechanisms to implement and monitor their memorandum of understanding (MOU); however, the performance metrics developed to assess its implementation do not adequately measure progress made toward its goals. VA and IHS have defined common goals for implementing the MOU and developed strategies to achieve them. They have also created two mechanisms to implement the MOU—12 workgroups with members from both agencies to address the goals of the MOU, and a Joint Implementation Task Force, comprised of VA and IHS officials, to oversee the MOU's implementation. These steps are consistent with practices that GAO has found enhance and sustain agency collaboration. The agencies have also developed three metrics aimed at measuring progress toward the MOU's goals. However, two of the three metrics are inadequate because their connection to any specific MOU goal is not clear and, while they include quantitative measures that tally the number of programs and activities increased or enhanced as a result of the MOU, they lack qualitative measures that would allow the agencies to assess the degree to which the desired results are achieved. The weaknesses in these metrics could limit the ability of VA and IHS managers to gauge progress and make decisions about whether to expand or modify their programs and activities.

VA and IHS face unique challenges associated with consulting with a large number of diverse, sovereign tribes to implement the MOU, and lack fully effective processes to overcome these complexities. VA and IHS officials told us the large number (566 federally recognized tribes) and differing customs and policy-making structures present logistical challenges in widespread implementation of the MOU within tribal communities. They also told us that tribal sovereignty—tribes' inherent right to govern and protect the health, safety, and welfare of tribal members—adds further complexity because tribes may choose whether or not to participate in MOU-related activities. Consistent with internal controls, VA and IHS have processes in place to consult with tribes on MOU- related activities through written correspondence and in-person meetings. However, according to tribal stakeholders GAO spoke with, these processes are often ineffective and have not always met the needs of the tribes, and the agencies have acknowledged that effective consultation has been challenging. For example, one tribal community expressed concern that agency correspondence is not always timely because it is sent to tribal leaders who are sometimes not the tribal members designated to take action on health care matters. Similarly, some tribal stakeholders told GAO that the agencies have not been responsive to tribal input and that sometimes they simply inform tribes of steps they have taken without consulting them. VA and IHS have taken steps to improve consultation with tribes. For example, VA has established an Office of Tribal Government Relations, through which it is developing relationships with tribal leaders and other tribal stakeholders. Additionally, in Alaska, VA has been consulting with a tribal health organization for insight on reaching tribes. However, given the concerns raised by the tribal stakeholders GAO spoke with, further efforts may be needed to enhance tribal consultation to implement and achieve the goals of the MOU.

ABBREVIATIONS

CMOP	Consolidated Mail Outpatient Pharmacy
EHR	electronic health record
HBPC	home-based primary care
IHS	Indian Health Service
MOU	memorandum of understanding
NCAI	National Congress of American Indians
OTGR	Office of Tribal Government Relations
VA	Department of Veterans Affairs

April 26, 2013

Congressional Requesters:

Native Americans (American Indians and Alaska Natives) have historically served in the military at a higher rate than any other ethnic group, according to the Department of Defense. Once separated from the military, some Native American veterans are eligible to receive health care services from both the Department of Veterans Affairs (VA) and the Indian Health Service (IHS), an agency within the Department of Health and Human Services.[1]

To improve the health status of Native American veterans through coordination, collaboration, and sharing of resources among VA, IHS, and tribes, in 2010, VA and IHS expanded upon a 2003 memorandum of understanding (MOU). This 2010 MOU outlined mutual goals for the agencies' collaboration and coordination of resources and care in providing health care services to Native American veterans. For example, it included provisions for joint contracts and purchasing agreements, sharing staff, ensuring providers in VA and IHS could access the electronic health records of shared patients, and the development of payment and reimbursement policies and mechanisms to support care delivered to Native American veterans eligible for care in both systems.

In a May 2012 congressional hearing, both VA and IHS reported that they have taken steps to collaborate to improve access to and quality of health care services for Native American veterans.[2] However, questions have been raised by members of Congress about the extent of collaboration between the two agencies. For example, a 2012 Senate report noted that stronger partnerships among VA, IHS, and tribally operated health facilities are essential to ensuring Native American veterans have access to health care services.[3] We were asked to examine how the agencies have implemented the MOU. In this report, we address the (1) extent to which VA and IHS have established mechanisms through which the MOU can be effectively implemented and monitored; and (2) key challenges that VA and IHS face in implementing the MOU, and the progress they have made in overcoming them.

To address both of these objectives, we reviewed the MOU and documentation related to the MOU's implementation, including periodic updates and descriptions of sharing agreements. We also reviewed the signed reimbursement agreement between VA and IHS as well as signed reimbursement agreements between VA and tribes.[4] We interviewed VA and

IHS officials, including VA's Director of the Office of Rural Health and Office of Tribal Government Relations, the IHS Chief Medical Officer, and leaders of 8 of 12 VA/IHS workgroups tasked with addressing and implementing the MOU to learn about the steps that have been taken to implement and monitor the MOU and any related challenges. We selected these eight workgroups because they were involved in addressing issues regarding agency coordination and sharing resources.[5]

To assess the MOU's implementation and related challenges, we took several actions to obtain the views of tribal communities. We attended a VA tribal consultation on MOU implementation at the National Indian Health Board Consumer Conference in Denver, Colorado, in September 2012, and attended the National Congress of American Indians (NCAI) Annual Conference in Sacramento, California, in October 2012. At the NCAI conference, we conducted listening sessions for tribal members to solicit their views on MOU implementation. We also interviewed various other tribal health representatives outside of the listening sessions and the conferences. In all, we interviewed 34 tribal members and other representatives (collectively referred to in this report as tribal stakeholders), including tribal leaders, tribal veterans, tribal health directors and administrators, and tribal health policy experts and consultants. The tribes represented in our interviews were geographically varied, including representation from 9 IHS Areas and 10 Veterans Integrated Service Networks and included representation from tribes that varied in size from approximately 500 members to 310,000 members. We cannot generalize findings from these interviews as representative of all tribal communities; however, we believe that patterns or issues identified in these interviews may illustrate issues that other tribes face as well.

To evaluate the extent to which VA and IHS have established mechanisms through which the MOU can be effectively implemented and monitored, we assessed this evidence against relevant criteria from our past work on interagency collaboration, practices from leading results-oriented public-sector organizations, and agency strategic planning.[6] To evaluate key challenges that VA and IHS face in implementing the MOU, and the progress they have made in overcoming them, we assessed this evidence against internal controls.[7]

We conducted this performance audit from July 2012 to April 2013 in accordance with generally accepted government auditing standards. Those standards require that we plan and perform the audit to obtain sufficient, appropriate evidence to provide a reasonable basis for our findings and conclusions based on our audit objectives. We believe that the evidence obtained provides a reasonable basis for our findings and conclusions based on our audit objectives.

BACKGROUND

Native American Veteran Demographics

While Native American veterans are geographically dispersed throughout the United States, the West and South regions contain the majority of the Native American veteran population, according to Census data. Some Native American veterans are members of the 566 federally recognized tribes that are distinct, independent political communities that possess certain powers of self-government, which we refer to as tribal sovereignty. Specifically, federally recognized tribes have government-to-government relationships with the United States, and are eligible for certain funding and services provided by the United States. In addition, some Native American veterans are members of the more than 400 Indian groups that are not recognized by the federal government (which we refer to in this report as non–federally recognized tribes).[8] Many—but not all—Native American veterans are dually eligible for health care services in VA and IHS. For example, a veteran who is a member of a non–federally recognized tribe may be eligible for VA health care services, but would not be eligible for IHS health care services.[9]

VA and IHS Structure and Benefits

VA is charged with providing health care services to the nation's veterans, and estimates that it will serve 6.3 million patients in fiscal year 2013. VA's fiscal year 2012 budget for medical care was approximately $54 billion. The department provides health care services at VA-operated facilities and through agreements with non-VA providers.[10] Veterans who served in the active military, naval or air service and who were discharged or released under conditions other than dishonorable are generally eligible for VA health care.

IHS is charged with providing health care to the approximately 2.1 million eligible Native Americans. IHS's fiscal year 2012 budget for medical care was approximately $3.9 billion. Similarly to VA, IHS provides health care services at IHS-operated facilities through direct care and pays for services from external providers through contract health services. In addition to IHS-operated facilities, some federally recognized tribes choose to operate their own health care facilities, which receive funding from IHS.[11] Like their IHS-operated counterparts, tribally operated facilities provide direct care services and pay for contract health services. IHS also provides funding through grants and contracts to nonprofit urban Native American organizations through the Urban Indian Health program in order to provide health care services to Native Americans living in urban areas.

VA and IHS Collaboration through Memorandums of Understanding

In 2003, VA and IHS signed an MOU to facilitate collaborative efforts in serving Native American veterans eligible for health care in both systems. In 2010, the agencies developed a more detailed MOU to further these efforts. The 2010 MOU contains provisions related to several areas of collaboration, including actions related to the following:

- *Joint contracts and purchasing agreements*: Development of standard, preapproved language for inclusion of one agency into contracts and purchasing agreements developed by the other agency; and processes to share information about sharing opportunities in early planning stages.
- *Sharing staff*: Establishment of joint credentialing and privileging, sharing specialty services, and arranging for temporary assignment of IHS Public Health Service commissioned officers to VA.
- *Electronic Health Record (EHR) access*: Establishment of standard mechanisms for VA providers to access records in IHS and tribally operated facilities, and vice versa, for patients receiving care in both systems.
- *Reimbursement*: Development of payment and reimbursement policies and mechanisms to support care delivered to dually eligible Native American veterans.

VA and IHS Tribal Consultation Policies

Executive Order 13175, issued on November 6, 2000, required federal agencies to establish regular and meaningful consultation and collaboration with Indian tribe officials in the development of federal policies that have tribal implications.[12] IHS issued a tribal consultation policy in 2006 to formalize the requirement to seek consultation and participation by Indian tribes in policy development and program activities. According to the policy, IHS will consult with Indian tribes to the extent practicable and permitted by law before any action is taken that will significantly affect Indian tribes. In November 2009, a Presidential Memorandum directed federal agencies to develop plans, after consultation with Indian tribes and tribal officials, for implementing the policies and directives of Executive Order 13175.[13] VA's plan included development of a tribal consultation policy, which the agency released in February 2011. VA's tribal consultation policy asserts that VA will establish meaningful consultation to develop, improve, or maintain partnerships with tribal communities. The policy states that consultation should be conducted before actions are taken but acknowledges there may not always be "sufficient time or resources to fully consult" on an issue.[14]

Best Practices and Internal Control Standards for Interagency Collaboration and Performance Monitoring

In past work we have reported on key practices to enhance and sustain interagency collaboration[15] including

- agreeing on roles and responsibilities;
- establishing compatible policies, procedures, and other means to operate across agency boundaries; and
- developing mechanisms to monitor, evaluate, and report on results.

Additionally, our past work has identified a range of mechanisms that the federal government uses to lead and implement interagency collaboration.[16] We found that regardless of the mechanisms used, there are key actions the government can take, including (1) having clear goals; (2) ensuring relevant participants are included in collaboration; and (3) specifying the resources—human, information, technology, physical, and financial—needed to initiate or sustain the collaboration. We have also found in past work on leading public-sector organizations and agency strategic planning that it is important to (1) define clear missions and desired outcomes; (2) use performance measures that are tangible, measurable, and clearly related to goals to gauge progress; and (3) use performance information as a basis for decision making.[17] Finally, internal control standards emphasize the importance of effective external communications that occur with groups that can have a serious effect on programs, projects, operations, and other activities, including budgeting and financing.[18]

VA AND IHS HAVE DEVELOPED MECHANISMS TO IMPLEMENT AND MONITOR THE MOU, BUT METRICS TO MONITOR PERFORMANCE DO NOT ADEQUATELY MEASURE PROGRESS TOWARD MOU GOALS

VA and IHS have documented common goals in their MOU, created 12 workgroups that are tasked with developing strategies to address the goals of the MOU, and created a Joint Implementation Task Force to coordinate tasks, develop implementation policy, and develop performance metrics and timelines—actions that are consistent with those we have found enhance and sustain agency collaboration. However, most of the performance metrics developed by VA and IHS to monitor the implementation of the MOU need to be more clearly related to the goals of the MOU in order to allow the agencies to gauge progress toward MOU goals.

VA and IHS Have Defined Common Goals and Created Mechanisms to Implement the MOU

Consistent with our past work on practices that can enhance and sustain collaboration, VA and IHS have defined common goals for implementing the MOU and developed specific strategies the agencies plan to take to achieve them. Table 1 summarizes the five goals in the 2010 MOU and selected strategies for implementing them.

VA and IHS have created two mechanisms to implement the MOU— workgroups and a Joint Implementation Task Force. We have reported that MOUs are most effective when they are regularly updated and monitored, actions that can be achieved by workgroups and task forces.[19]

Table 1. Goals and Associated Strategies in the Department of Veterans Affairs (VA) / Indian Health Service (IHS) 2010 Memorandum of Understanding (MOU)

MOU goal	Selected strategies to achieve goal
1. Increase access to and improve quality of health care and services to the mutual benefit of both agencies. Effectively leverage the strengths of the VA and IHS at the national and local levels to afford the delivery of optimal clinical care.	• Share specialty services • Develop joint credentialing and privileging of staff • Develop joint training initiatives • Develop and implement new models of care using new technologies, including telehealth services
2. Promote patient-centered collaboration and facilitate communication among VA, IHS, Native American veterans, tribal facilities, and Urban Indian Clinics.	• Establish mechanism to share electronic health records for patients receiving care in both systems and from tribally operated facilities • Improve the delivery of care through sharing of care processes, programs, and services (for example, post-traumatic stress disorder and diabetes management)
3. In consultation with tribes at the regional and local levels, establish effective partnerships and sharing agreements among VA headquarters and facilities, IHS headquarters and IHS, tribal, and Urban Indian Health programs in support of Native American veterans.	• Develop standard preapproved language for inclusion of one agency into the other agency's existing contracts • Develop preapproved templates for agreements to facilitate local, regional, and national collaboration
4. Ensure that appropriate resources are identified and available to support programs for Native American veterans.	• Develop payment and reimbursement policies and mechanisms for veterans receiving care in both systems
5. Improve health promotion and disease prevention services to Native Americans to address community-based wellness.	• Improve the delivery of care through sharing of care processes, programs, and services (for example, post-traumatic stress disorder and diabetes management)

Source: GAO analysis of information provided by VA and IHS.

Workgroups

VA and IHS created 12 workgroups tasked with responsibility for implementing and developing strategies to address the goals of the MOU, such as interoperability of health information technology; developing payment and reimbursement agreements; and sharing of care processes, programs, and services.[20] Each workgroup includes members from VA and IHS, a step that can foster mutual trust across diverse agency cultures and facilitate frequent communication across agencies to enhance shared understanding of collaboration goals, according to our previous work on interagency collaboration. According to VA and IHS officials, most of the workgroup members volunteered to serve on the workgroups and were self-selected, and VA officials told us that they have consulted with tribes on how to increase tribal participation in the workgroups. The agencies also told us that some workgroup members were asked to participate because of their subject-matter expertise.[21]

Table 2. Goals of Eight Workgroups Interviewed and Corresponding Department of Veterans Affairs (VA) / Indian Health Service (IHS) Memorandum of Understanding (MOU) Goals

Workgroup	Goals	Crosswalk to MOU goals
Coordination of Care	• Increase access to and quality of care. • Promote patient-centered collaboration and increase coordination of care, including comanagement of dual- eligible veterans. Work with tribal urban organizations.	Goal 1: Increase access to and improve quality of health care and services to the mutual benefit of both agencies. Goal 2: Promote patient-centered collaboration and facilitate communication.
Health Information Technology	• Improve care through the development of health information technology. • Establish system to share electronic health records.	Goal 1: Increase access to and improve quality of health care and services to the mutual benefit of both agencies. Goal 2: Promote patient-centered collaboration and facilitate communication.
System Level	• Plan and implement system-level resources to share information about contracts and purchasing arrangements.	Goal 3: Establish effective partnerships and sharing agreements. Goal 4: Ensure that appropriate resources are identified and available to support programs.
Payment and Reimbursement	• Design system to ensure VA and IHS systems are compatible for the billing and collecting process under contracts or agreements.	Goal 4: Ensure that appropriate resources are identified and available to support programs.
Sharing of Care Process, Programs and Services	• Several MOU goals, including improving access to and quality of care for post-traumatic stress disorder	Goal 1: Increase access to and improve quality of health care and services to the mutual benefit of both agencies.

Table 2. (Continued)

Workgroup	Goals	Crosswalk to MOU goals
	among Native American veterans. • Conduct outreach to tribal areas in areas such as public health and suicide prevention. • Develop and update suicide prevention training. • Provide IHS pharmacists access to VA programs to streamline pharmacy dispensing activities. Coordinate and collaborate to improve the lives of elderly and frail Native Americans, and increase access to VA's home-based primary care program.	Goal 2: Promote patient-centered collaboration and facilitate communication. Goal 3: Establish effective partnerships and sharing agreements. Goal 5: Improve health-promotion and disease-prevention services to Native Americans to address community-based wellness.
Training and Recruitment	• Increase capability and improve quality through training and workforce development, sharing of educational and training opportunities, and the development of joint training initiatives. • Increase access to care through sharing of staff and enhanced recruitment and retention of professional staff.	Goal 1: Increase access to and improve quality of health care and services to the mutual benefit of both agencies.
Alaska	• Increase access to services and benefits of IHS and VA. • Improve coordination of care, including comanagement, for Native American veterans served by both VA and tribal organizations. • Increase availability of services, in accordance with law, by the development of payment and reimbursement policies and mechanisms.	Goal 1: Increase access to and improve quality of health care and services to the mutual benefit of both agencies. Goal 2: Promote patient-centered collaboration and facilitate communication. Goal 3: Establish effective partnerships and sharing agreements Goal 4: Ensure that appropriate resources are identified and available to support programs. Goal 5: Improve health-promotion and disease-prevention services to Native Americans to address community-based wellness.

Workgroup	Goals	Crosswalk to MOU goals
Oversight	• Set priorities for the Joint Implementation Task Force to identify the strategies and plans for accomplishing the tasks and aims of the MOU, and help the task force follow the strategy and plans of the MOU. • Meet with and receive updates from other workgroups and elevate issues identified by the workgroups. • Develop reports on progress in implementing the MOU.	Goal 1: Increase access to and improve quality of health care and services to the mutual benefit of both agencies. Goal 2: Promote patient-centered collaboration and facilitate communication. Goal 3: Establish effective partnerships and sharing agreements. Goal 4: Ensure that appropriate resources are identified and available to support programs. Goal 5: Improve health-promotion and disease-prevention services to Native Americans to address community-based wellness.

Source: GAO evaluation of interviews with workgroups and agency officials and the MOU.

Goals established by each workgroup appear to be aligned with MOU goals. Specifically, all eight of the workgroups we interviewed described goals that were consistent with the MOU goals.[22] Table 2 lists each workgroup we interviewed and provides a crosswalk between workgroup goals and the corresponding MOU goal or strategy.

Joint Implementation Task Force

VA and IHS created the Joint Implementation Task Force to oversee the overall implementation of the MOU. This task force comprises officials from both agencies including from the Office of the Secretary of Veterans Affairs, the IHS Chief Medical Officer, and the director of VA's Office of Tribal Government Relations, and is scheduled to meet quarterly. It develops implementation policy and procedures for policy-related issues identified by the workgroups; creates performance metrics and timelines, evaluates progress; and compiles an annual report on progress in MOU implementation. Creating a mechanism, such as a task force, intended not only to address issues arising from potential incompatibility of standards and policies across agencies but also to monitor, evaluate, and report on MOU results, can help to facilitate collaboration, according to our previous work on interagency collaboration.

Table 3. GAO Evaluation of Performance Metrics and Measures Developed to Monitor Progress toward Department of Veterans Affairs (VA) / Indian Health Service (IHS) Memorandum of Understanding (MOU) Goals

Metric	Measures	GAO evaluation
Metric 1: Programs increased or enhanced as a result of the VA-IHS MOU	1. Number of programs enhanced and increased 2. Number of events and activities to increase or enhance the programs 3. Number of veterans impacted 4. Met purposes of MOU (yes or no) 5. Met intent of MOU (yes or no) 6. Level of VA-IHS-Tribal participation (poor, fair, good, excellent)	Inadequate Tangible and measurable, but not clearly aligned with an MOU goal and would not allow agencies to determine how well MOU goals are achieved.
Metric 2: Outreach activities that are the result of MOU partnerships	1. Types of outreach events held 2. Number of outreach events held 3. Number of veterans and others (families, caregivers) impacted 4. Met purposes of MOU (yes or no) 5. Met intent of MOU (yes or no) 6. Level of VA-IHS-Tribal participation (poor, fair, good, excellent)	Inadequate Tangible and measurable but not clearly aligned with an MOU goal, and would not allow agencies to determine how well MOU goals are achieved.
Metric 3: Development of reimbursement agreements and sharing agreements as a result of the MOU	1. Number of sharing agreements developed 2. Number of tribes impacted 3. Number of reimbursement agreements developed 4. Number of tribes impacted 5. Met purposes of MOU (yes or no) 6. Met intent of MOU (yes or no) 7. Level of VA-IHS-Tribal participation (poor, fair, good, excellent)	Adequate Tangible and measureable, aligned with an MOU goal, and allows the agencies to measure progress toward goals three and four.

Source: GAO analysis of information provided by VA and IHS.

Note: The five MOU goals are:

(1) Increase access to and improve quality of health care and services to the mutual benefit of both agencies. Effectively leverage the strengths of the VA and IHS at the national and local levels to afford the delivery of optimal clinical care.
(2) Promote patient-centered collaboration and facilitate communication among VA, IHS, Native American veterans, tribal facilities, and Urban Indian Clinics.
(3) In consultation with tribes at the regional and local levels, establish effective partnerships and sharing agreements among VA headquarters and facilities, IHS headquarters and IHS, tribal, and Urban Indian Health programs in support of Native American veterans.
(4) Ensure that appropriate resources are identified and available to support programs for Native American veterans.
(5) Improve health promotion and disease prevention services to Native Americans to address community-based wellness.

VA and IHS Performance Metrics Do Not Adequately Measure Progress on the MOU Goals

The process developed by the Joint Implementation Task Force to monitor the implementation of the MOU includes obtaining data on three performance metrics; however, two of the three metrics do not allow the agencies to measure progress toward the MOU's goals. Our previous work has found that successful performance metrics should be tangible and measureable, clearly aligned with specific goals, and demonstrate the degree to which desired results are achieved.[23] Although all three of the performance metrics are tangible and measurable, only one is also clearly aligned with a specific goal and defined in a manner that would allow the agencies to adequately measure the degree to which desired results are achieved. The other two metrics are inadequate because their connection to a specific goal is not clear and they lack qualitative measures that would allow the agencies to measure the degree to which desired results are achieved. For example, one MOU goal is to increase access to and improve quality of health care services, but none of the metrics mention any targets specifically linked to increased access or improved quality of care. Another goal is to establish effective partnerships and sharing agreements among the agencies and the tribes in support of Native American veterans. Although one of the metrics appears to be related to this goal, in that it is focused on measuring the number of outreach activities that are a result of partnerships, it lacks measures to determine how well the outreach activities are meeting the goal of establishing effective partnerships or other potential goals to which the outreach may contribute, such as facilitating communication among VA, IHS, veterans, and tribally operated facilities. The metrics would therefore not enable VA and IHS to determine how well these specific goals are being achieved. Table 3 describes the performance metrics and performance measures and our evaluation of them.

Using these metrics, the agencies have issued MOU progress reports, but the metrics included in the reports generally are not clearly tied specifically to the goals of the MOU, nor do they allow the agencies to determine how well MOU goals have been achieved. Leading public- sector organizations have found that metrics that are clearly linked to goals and allow determination of how well goals are achieved are key steps to becoming more results-oriented. For example:

- According to the agencies' fiscal year 2011-2012 metrics report,[24] for Metric 1 (programs increased or enhanced as a result of the MOU), more than 15 programs were enhanced or increased as the result of the MOU, and 440 events and activities occurred that increased or enhanced the programs. The report then provides examples of programs that have been enhanced, such as a care coordination program in which a registered nurse "works with Indian Health, Tribal Programs, and other agencies and hospitals through direct meetings at various facilities to ensure communication and improved care." However, the report does not always describe information that would allow the agencies to determine how well each activity contributes to meeting MOU goals. For instance, in the description of an enhanced care coordination program noted above, the report does not indicate how the agencies determined that communication has improved among participants. Absent this information, it is not clear how the agencies could draw conclusions about whether improved communication has actually been facilitated and therefore how well the activity contributed to meeting the MOU goal of promoting patient- centered collaboration and facilitating communication.

- According to the metrics report, for Metric 2 (outreach activities increased or enhanced as a result of MOU partnerships), eight types of activities were increased or enhanced. However, the report lists only seven types of outreach and does not include enough information to determine how well the outreach contributes to meeting MOU goals. For example, one outreach activity cited in the report, "Outreach to promote implementation of new technologies," includes the activity "VA Office of Telehealth Services (OTS) Coordinator participated in

Web-ex sessions with IHS on use of technology to improve patient care." Although not stated in the report, this activity appears to help implement the MOU strategy of enhancing access through the development and implementation of new models of care using new technologies, including telehealth, related to the MOU goals of promoting patient-centered care and increasing access to care. However, while outreach activities are measurable and tangible, and might help to achieve goals of the MOU, the report does not state how the agencies will determine whether the sessions actually were effective in improving patient care or increasing access, information that is necessary to allow the agencies to tell how well the activity helps achieve the MOU goals.

- For each metric, the agencies report whether the activities "met the purpose of the MOU," "met the intent of the MOU," and whether the "level of VA-IHS-Tribal participation" was poor, fair, good, or excellent. While determining whether the agencies' activities meet the purpose and intent of the MOU is a critical step, and obtaining tribal participation is consistent with MOU goals, the report does not describe how these determinations were made. Agency officials told us that these determinations were made subjectively by each workgroup while keeping in mind the goals and strategies in the MOU.

The weaknesses we found in these performance metrics could limit the ability of VA and IHS managers to gauge progress and make decisions about whether to expand or modify programs or activities, because the agencies will not have information on how well programs are supporting MOU goals. VA and IHS officials told us that they developed these performance metrics because the initial performance metrics, drafted by the workgroups themselves and other VA and IHS staff, varied in quality. The three metrics and measures were intended to provide some simple, measurable ways for workgroups to report on their progress. However, they also acknowledged that there were weaknesses in the measures and told us that refining these performance metrics is a priority. According to the officials, they plan to revise workgroup metrics by April 2013 and on a continuous basis going forward. In doing so, they plan to consult subject-matter experts and existing VA and IHS performance metrics, for example, prevention of hospital admissions in home-based primary care programs.

VA AND IHS LACK EFFECTIVE PROCESSES TO OVERCOME THE CHALLENGES OF CONSULTING WITH A LARGE NUMBER OF DIVERSE, SOVEREIGN TRIBES

Mainly because of the large number of diverse tribal communities and tribal sovereignty, VA and IHS face unique challenges associated with coordinating and communicating to implement the MOU. VA and IHS have processes in place for consulting with tribes, but these measures fall short in several respects and do not ensure such consultation is effective.

VA and IHS Face Challenges Implementing the MOU Related to the Large Number of Diverse, Sovereign Tribes

VA and IHS officials told us the large number (566) of federally recognized tribes and differing customs and policy-making structures present logistical challenges in widespread implementation of the MOU within tribal communities.[25] For instance, according to some VA officials, in some tribes as a matter of protocol, an agency must be invited on tribal lands or be sponsored by a council member in order to address a tribal council. Such a policy could add administrative processes that might delay implementation and require greater sensitivity from agency officials, adding to the challenge of consulting with tribes. As another example, the title or position of the tribal person designated to make decisions regarding health care may differ from tribe to tribe, complicating the decision-making process among VA, IHS, and tribes. VA officials told us in some tribes, for example, a tribal leader may have several roles, only one of which is making decisions on health care, whereas in other tribes there may be a tribal health director whom the tribal leader has designated to manage health care in the tribal community. Potentially, these differences can affect the speed and degree at which collective decisions can be made.

In addition, VA and IHS officials noted that tribal sovereignty further adds to the logistical complexity of the efforts of the agencies to implement the MOU. Tribal sovereignty includes the inherent right to govern and protect the health, safety, and welfare of tribal members. Indian tribes have a legal and political government-to-government relationship with the federal government, meaning federal agencies interact with tribes as governments, not as special interest groups or individuals. VA and IHS officials told us that because of tribal sovereignty, tribally operated facilities may choose whether or not to participate in a particular opportunity for collaboration related to the MOU, which makes it challenging to achieve some of the goals of the MOU. VA and IHS can inform tribes of an opportunity but cannot require them to participate. For example:

- In order to meet the MOU goal to establish standard mechanisms for access to electronic health record (EHR) information for shared patients, VA and IHS have coordinated to adapt their information technology systems to allow them both to participate in the eHealth Exchange, a national effort led by the Department of Health and Human Services for sharing EHR information.[26] However, EHR workgroup members told us that some tribally operated facilities have opted to use an off-the-shelf product in place of the IHS system, which the workgroup members do not have the resources to support.
- In another instance, as a part of their efforts to meet the MOU goal to establish effective partnerships and sharing agreements, VA and IHS are working to implement VA's Consolidated Mail Outpatient Pharmacy (CMOP) throughout IHS. Workgroup members assigned to these activities said they plan to implement the program in all IHS-operated facilities by spring 2013 but cannot require tribally operated facilities to participate. Some smaller tribal communities with more limited postal access are not interested in using the CMOP program, according to the workgroup members.

VA and IHS Processes in Place to Overcome the Complexities Associated with Consulting with Tribes Do Not Always Ensure Effective Consultation

VA and IHS communicate MOU-related information with the tribes through written correspondence, in-person meetings, and other steps, as is consistent with internal controls calling for effective external communications with groups that can have a serious effect on programs and other activities; however, according to tribal stakeholders we interviewed, these methods for consultation have not always met the needs of the tribal communities, and the agencies have acknowledged that effective consultation has been challenging.

Written Correspondence

VA and IHS send written correspondence (known as "Dear Tribal Leader" letters) regarding the MOU to tribal communities. However, the agencies have acknowledged that because of the large and diverse nature of the tribes, they have struggled to reach the tribal member designated to make health care decisions with information about the MOU. Both VA officials and members of tribal communities told us that, because tribal leaders are not always the tribal person designated to make decisions regarding health care, the "Dear Tribal Leader" letters may not always make their way to tribal members designated to take action on health care matters. VA officials told us that their formal consultation is conducted with tribal leaders. However, these officials also noted that, in addition to the letters sent to tribal leaders, they have a network of contacts within each tribe that includes, among others, tribal health directors, and this network receives concurrent notice of communication with tribal leaders via conference calls, listservs, and newsletters. IHS officials said sometimes, in addition to the tribal leader, they may also send letters to, or otherwise communicate directly with, tribal health program directors if they know of them. However, they also noted they do not maintain a specific record— such as a listserv—of tribal health program directors. Without reaching the tribal members responsible for decision-making on healthcare matters, VA and IHS may not always be effectively communicating with tribes about the status of the MOU and its related activities nor be obtaining tribal feedback that is critical with respect to implementation of the MOU.

Likewise, seven tribal stakeholders we spoke with noted similar concerns regarding the "Dear Tribal Leader" letters as VA and IHS. For example, one tribal stakeholder said letters should go to a specific person, such as a tribal health director, to ensure that the information is seen by the right people in a timely manner. It may take the tribes time to pass along letters sent only to tribal leaders to the tribal health director or other appropriate people, by which point any deadlines included in the correspondence could be missed. Once the information has reached the tribal leader, tribes bear the responsibility to ensure it is passed on to the appropriate audience in a timely manner.

Another specific concern tribal stakeholders that we spoke with expressed relating to written correspondence was that the agencies sometimes use the letters to simply inform them of steps the agencies have taken without consulting the tribes, as called for by the agencies' tribal consultation policies. For example, some tribal stakeholders said VA and IHS did not include them in the original development of the 2010 MOU, even though the goals and activities in the MOU could directly affect them. According to 10 of the tribal stakeholders we spoke with, tribes should have been included in developing the MOU, which addresses proposed plans, policies, and programmatic actions that may affect tribes. For example, the MOU seeks to improve delivery of health care by developing and implementing new models of care using new technologies, including telehealth services such as telepsychiatry. Instead, the agencies solicited tribal comments after the agencies had signed the MOU. According to two tribal stakeholders, the agencies were not responsive to the comments provided on the MOU. One stakeholder said their comments were not acknowledged upon receipt nor did IHS ever follow up on the issues raised by their comments. The stakeholder suggested IHS designate a point person to track feedback and ensure follow-up. VA and IHS officials told us that they did not hold tribal consultation meetings before the signing of the MOU because they viewed the MOU as an agency-to-agency agreement rather than as an agreement between the agencies and the various tribes.

In-Person Meetings

VA and IHS officials said they hold quarterly meetings with tribal communities and also attend events, such as conferences held by Native American interest organizations. Three tribal stakeholders told us that when the agencies have held consultation meetings, the meetings are not interactive enough—stating that agency officials speak for the majority of the time—and that VA does not provide enough information prior to these meetings. These tribal stakeholders said providing information ahead of time could allow tribes to better prepare for meetings, discuss issues as a tribe beforehand, and determine which tribal members should attend. If tribal officials with the authority and desire to work with VA and IHS do not receive needed information on opportunities because of an ineffective consultation process, local facility leadership may not have readily available access to information necessary to examine which collaborative opportunities are present, and thus VA and IHS may be hindered in their efforts to coordinate health care for Native American veterans.

VA and IHS are undertaking other efforts designed to enhance consultation with tribes. These include the following steps:

- In January 2011, VA established the Office of Tribal Government Relations (OTGR) to serve as the point of contact for tribes. According to VA officials, this office conducted four consultation meetings in 2012 and employed five field staff to help manage communication with tribal communities and to work with IHS on local MOU implementation efforts.

- In February 2011, VA released the agency's tribal consultation policy. VA officials said they are developing a report that will explain the process for evaluating comments from tribes and making decisions based on them. The officials expect the report to be released to the public in the spring of 2013.

- The agencies have made more local efforts to communicate with tribes, which have led to some success. For example, agency officials and tribal stakeholders noted that the workgroup assigned to implement MOU activities in Alaska used successful methods for working with tribes. The Alaska workgroup told us they cultivated a relationship with an Alaskan tribal health organization in order to get advice on the appropriate customs for consulting with individual tribes there. In addition, the workgroup said they scheduled consultation meetings in conjunction with other meetings, which would limit the amount of travel tribal community members would need to undertake. VA employees also took cultural awareness training, and VA officials visited Alaska to demonstrate the agency's dedication to providing care to Native American veterans, which, according to the workgroup, led to buy-in from tribal communities. VA and Alaskan tribes have signed 26 reimbursement agreements.

Some tribal stakeholders that we spoke with have acknowledged the steps taken by the agencies thus far as positive but in some cases expressed concerns regarding tribal consultation. In the case of the tribes working with the Alaska workgroup, one stakeholder praised VA's efforts to work with tribal health organizations to communicate with tribes. In another example, two tribal stakeholders said they approved of OTGR's establishment as an office dedicated to Native American veterans' issues. However, four tribal stakeholders expressed concerns that, despite the creation of OTGR, VA still has not always been effective in its efforts to consult with tribes or be responsive to tribal input provided during consultation. For example, one stakeholder questioned whether consultation was done with every tribe and described VA's consultation process as sporadic. This stakeholder's concern implies that VA's outreach efforts may not be systematically reaching all tribal communities. However, VA officials told us that, in addition to issuing notices in the Federal Register and Dear Tribal Leader letters, they have a systematic process of hosting training summits for tribes and scheduling regular conference calls and presentations to tribal leadership. In another instance, one tribal community member said OTGR lacks—and thus cannot disperse to tribes—the technical knowledge necessary for tribes to partner with VA on activities such as negotiating reimbursement agreements. VA officials noted that OTGR staff may not always be technical experts on a given topic but said they are able to identify those experts and play a key role in linking tribes with them.

CONCLUSION

Coordination between VA and IHS is essential to ensuring that high-quality health care is provided to dually eligible Native American veterans. While the 2010 MOU includes common goals that should facilitate agency coordination, and the agencies have created workgroups tasked to implement the MOU, we found that a critical mechanism for monitoring the implementation of the MOU, the agreement's performance metrics, has weaknesses. Specifically, the inadequacies we found in performance metrics could limit the agencies' ability to measure progress towards MOU goals and ultimately make decisions about programs or activities.

Overcoming the challenges related to working with a large number of diverse, sovereign tribes is also essential to successfully achieving the goals of the MOU. Although steps have been taken to consult with tribes regarding the MOU and related activities, consultation has not always been effective in assuring that the people designated to make health care decisions in each tribe are reached and tribes are included in planning and implementation efforts. Ineffective consultation with tribal communities could delay or limit potential VA, IHS, and tribal community partnerships to achieve the goals of the MOU and could hinder agency efforts to gain support for MOU activities and address the health care needs of Native American veterans.

RECOMMENDATIONS FOR EXECUTIVE ACTION

To ensure the health care needs of Native American veterans are addressed most efficiently and effectively, we recommend that the Secretary of Veterans Affairs and Secretary of Health and Human Services take the following two actions:

- As the agencies move forward with revising the MOU's performance metrics and measures, ensure that the revised metrics and measures allow decision makers to gauge whether achievement of the metrics and measures supports attainment of MOU goals.
- Develop processes to better ensure that consultation with tribes is effective, including the following:
  - A process to identify the appropriate tribal members with whom to communicate MOU-related information, which should include methods for keeping such identification up-to-date.
  - A process to clearly outline and communicate to tribal communities the agencies' response to tribal input, including any changes in policies and programs or other effects that result from incorporating tribal input.
  - A process to establish timelines for releasing information to tribal communities to ensure they have enough time to review and provide input or, in the case of meetings, determine the appropriate tribal member to attend the event.

AGENCY COMMENTS

We provided draft copies of this report to VA and the Department of Health and Human Services for review. Both agencies concurred with our recommendations. In addition, VA provided us with comments on the draft report, as well as general and technical comments, which were incorporated in the draft as appropriate.

Randall Williamson
Director, Health Care

End Notes

[1] According to the U.S. Census Bureau, in 2011 approximately 150,000 individuals identified themselves as Native American veterans. This includes only individuals who identified as American Indian or Alaska Native alone and not in combination with another racial group. Therefore, it likely underestimates the number of Native American veterans.

[2] *Oversight Hearing on Programs and Services for Native Veterans*: hearing before the Committee on Indian Affairs, United States Senate, 112th Cong (May 24, 2012).

[3] S. Rep. No. 112-168, at 45 (May 22, 2012).

[4] VA is required to reimburse federally and tribally operated facilities for health care services provided to beneficiaries who are eligible for such services from VA. 25 U.S.C. § 1645(c).

[5] The eight workgroups we interviewed were: (1) Coordination of Care; (2) Health Information Technology; (3) System Level; (4) Payment and Reimbursement; (5) Sharing of Care Process, Programs and Services; (6) Training and Recruitment; (7) Oversight; and (8) Alaska. VA and IHS count the Training and Recruitment Workgroup as two separate workgroups. However, because these two workgroups share similar goals, an IHS official told us they combined them into one workgroup, and for the purposes of this report we considered them as one workgroup. There are also four other workgroups covering: (1) Services and Benefits, (2) New Technologies; (3) Cultural Competency and Awareness; and (4) Emergency and Disaster Preparedness. We did not interview these workgroups because they did not directly relate to our objectives.

[6] GAO, *Results-Oriented Government: Practices That Can Help Enhance and Sustain Collaboration among Federal Agencies*, GAO-06-15 (Washington, D.C.: Oct. 21, 2005); *Managing for Results: Key Considerations for Implementing Interagency Collaborative Mechanisms*, GAO-12-1022 (Washington, D.C.: Sept. 27, 2012); *Executive Guide: Effectively Implementing the Government Performance and Results Act*, GAO/GGD-96-118 (Washington, D.C.: June 1996); and *Agencies' Strategic Plans Under GPRA: Key Questions to Facilitate Congressional Review*, GAO/GGD-10.1.16 (Washington, D.C.: May 1997).

[7] GAO, *Internal Control Standards: Internal Control Management and Evaluation Tool*, GAO-01-1008G (Washington, D.C.: August 2001).

[8] For more information on federal funding for non–federally recognized tribes, see GAO, *Indian Issues: Federal Funding for Non-Federally Recognized Tribes*, GAO-12-348 (Washington, D.C.: Apr. 12, 2012).

[9] To be eligible for IHS health care services, an individual must be closely affiliated with a federally recognized tribe, as evidenced by such factors as membership; enrollment; residence on tax-exempt land; ownership of restricted property; active participation in tribal affairs; or other relevant factors indicative of Native American descent. See 42 C.F.R. § 136.12.

[10] To manage its provision of health care services for eligible veterans, VA operates a system of annual patient enrollment in accordance with eight listed priorities. See 38 U.S.C. § 1705.

[11] Under the Indian Self-Determination and Education Assistance Act, as amended, federally recognized tribes can enter into self-determination contracts or self-governance compacts with the Secretary of Health and Human Services to take over administration of IHS programs for Native Americans previously administered by IHS on their behalf because of their status as Indians. Self-governance compacts allow tribes to consolidate and assume administration of all programs, services, activities, and competitive grants administered throughout IHS, or portions thereof, that are carried out for the benefit of Native Americans because of their status as Indians. Self determination contracts allow tribes to assume administration of a program, programs, or portions thereof. See 25 U.S.C. §§ 450f(a) (self-determination contracts)and 458aaa-4(b)(1) (self-governance compacts).

[12] Federal agencies are required to consult with Alaska Native corporations on the same basis as Indian tribes under Executive Order 13175. Pub. L. No. 108-199, div. H, § 161, 118 Stat. 3, 452 (2004), as amended.

[13] See 74 Fed. Reg. 57,881 (Nov. 9, 2009).

[14] According to the policy, the principal focus of consultation is the tribally designated "tribal official" and that consultation will be initiated by means of written notification.

[15] GAO-06-15 and GAO-12-1022.

[16] GAO-12-1022.

[17] GAO/GGD-10.1.16 and GAO/GGD-96-118 (for this report, GAO studied a number of leading public-sector organizations that were successfully becoming more results- oriented,

including state governments such as in Florida, Texas, and Virginia; and foreign governments such as in Australia and the United Kingdom).

[18] GAO-01-1008G.

[19] GAO-12-1022.

[20] The 12 workgroups are: (1) Coordination of Care; (2) Health Information Technology; (3) System Level; (4) Payment and Reimbursement; (5) Sharing of Care Process, Programs and Services; (6) Training and Recruitment; (7) Oversight; (8) Alaska; (9) Services and Benefits; (10) New Technologies; (11) Cultural Competency and Awareness; and (12) Emergency and Disaster Preparedness.

[21] The officials told us that in cases where a workgroup lacks authority to implement an MOU task, workgroup members would notify MOU coordinators designated by each agency, who would then notify the appropriate agency officials about the issue.

[22] We did not interview 4 workgroups because they did not directly relate to our objectives: (1) Services and Benefits; (2) New Technologies; (3) Cultural Competency and Awareness; and (4) Emergency and Disaster Preparedness.

[23] GAO/GGD-96-118 and GAO/GGD-10.1.16.

[24] Department of Veterans Affairs and Indian Health Service, *Department of Veterans Affairs (VA) Indian Health Service (IHS) Memorandum of Understanding (MOU) Metrics Report— Fiscal Year (FY) 2011/2012.*

[25] In addition to the federally recognized tribes, there are more than 400 non–federally recognized tribes. Although these non–federally recognized tribes may not receive IHS funding and members may not be eligible for IHS services, VA has an obligation to serve their members who are eligible for VA services.

[26] The eHealth Exchange is a set of standards, services, and policies that enable the secure exchange of health information over the Internet.

In: Native American Veterans' Access ...   ISBN: 978-1-63463-064-1
Editor: Lorrie Hobbs   © 2014 Nova Science Publishers, Inc.

Chapter 2

HEALTH CARE ACCESS: IMPROVED OVERSIGHT, ACCOUNTABILITY, AND PRIORITIZATION CAN IMPROVE ACCESS FOR NATIVE AMERICAN VETERANS[*]

United States Government Accountability Office

WHY GAO DID THIS STUDY

Native Americans who have served in the military may be eligible for health care services from both VA and IHS, but according to reports some have had problems accessing care. In 2010 these two agencies expanded upon an memorandum of understanding (MOU) designed to improve Native American veterans' access to care at their facilities. GAO was asked to examine how the memorandum of understanding (MOU) has increased access to care.

This report examines: (1) the actions that VA and IHS have taken to implement the provisions in the 2010 memorandum of understanding (MOU) related to access to care for Native American veterans, and (2) what is known about how access to care for Native American veterans has improved. To

---

[*] This is an edited, reformatted and augmented version of the United States Government Accountability Office publication, GAO-14-489, dated June 2014.

conduct this work, GAO reviewed agency documents and VA and IHS reimbursement data and interviewed VA and IHS officials. GAO also visited three sites selected to reflect geographic variation to learn about access to care locally through interviews with regional VA and IHS officials, health facility officials, and Native American veterans and their tribal representatives. GAO also contacted other individuals who help Native American veterans seek enrollment in the VA to obtain their insights about improvements in access to care.

WHAT GAO RECOMMENDS

GAO recommends that VA and IHS establish written policy or guidance designating specific roles and responsibilities for agency staff to hold leadership accountable and improve implementation and oversight of the MOU. VA and IHS agreed with GAO's recommendation.

WHAT GAO FOUND

The Department of Veterans Affairs (VA) and the Indian Health Service (IHS) have taken a variety of actions to improve access to care for Native American veterans under their 2010 memorandum of understanding (MOU); however according to stakeholders, these agencies face substantial implementation challenges. VA and IHS have taken actions to (1) strengthen outreach and enrollment through information sharing and training; (2) expand services through national and local projects; (3) increase training about cultural competency for staff at VA and IHS facilities; and (4) establish reimbursement agreements that allow VA to reimburse IHS facilities for services provided to veterans. However, in each of these areas challenges remain, such as insufficient data to identify Native American veterans for outreach, obstacles to reaching those who live in very remote areas, and technological challenges such as lack of Internet connectivity or phone lines.

While VA and IHS have taken actions to increase access, the oversight, accountability, and prioritization of MOU implementation are lacking. Specifically:

- Oversight is inconsistent: In 2013, the officials tasked with oversight of the implementation of the MOU did not meet and did not systematically evaluate the progress of MOU implementation.
- Written policies and guidance are lacking: According to officials, the only documentation outlining the procedures to report VA and IHS progress on implementation efforts is contained in a set of training slides used in a December 2012 training session, and these slides have not been formalized in written policy or guidance.
- Prioritization of MOU implementation is lacking: Leadership of VA and IHS have not made MOU implementation a priority, which threatens the ability of the two agencies to move forward in implementing the MOU. Key officials attributed this, in part, to their perception that their non-MOU related responsibilities had a higher priority.

Without consistent oversight, formal policy or guidance on responsibilities for MOU implementation, and the prioritization of MOU implementation, VA and IHS leadership do not have reasonable assurance that the objectives of the MOU related to access to care are being addressed.

Native American veterans and their representatives that GAO contacted reported mixed views on whether access to care has improved over the past 3 years. Although a majority reported that access to care had improved, others either said that that they did not think it had improved or were unsure. For example, 53 of 102 Native American veterans representatives GAO contacted reported that in the last 3 years there had been an increase in the number of Native American veterans accessing health care at VA or IHS-funded facilities; however, 12 felt there had been no change, and 36 said they did not know.

ABBREVIATIONS

HHS	Department of Health and Human Services
IHS	Indian Health Service
MOU	memorandum of understanding
ORH	Office of Rural Health
OTGR	Office of Tribal Government Relations
PTSD	post-traumatic stress disorder
THP	Tribal Health Program

TVR	Tribal Veterans Representative
VA	Department of Veterans Affairs
VISN	Veterans Integrated Service Network

***

June 10, 2014

Congressional Requesters

Native Americans historically have served in the military at a higher rate than any other ethnic group, according to the Department of Defense.[1] Once separated from the military, some Native American veterans are eligible to receive health care services from both the Department of Veterans Affairs (VA) and the Indian Health Service (IHS), an agency within the Department of Health and Human Services (HHS).

According to Congressional testimony and media reports, Native American veterans have had problems accessing care in both VA and IHS. For example, some Native American veterans report being turned away from both VA and IHS-funded facilities because of confusion among facility staff over eligibility requirements.[2] Native American veterans have also reported that a lack of cultural competency regarding tribal practices and the needs of veterans can affect their access to care at VA and IHS-funded facilities. For example, it has been reported that a lack of understanding of traditional healing practices or the varied needs of each tribe can be a barrier to accessing care at VA, and a lack of clinical expertise on certain veterans' care issues— such as expertise on how to treat post-traumatic stress disorder (PTSD)—can make it difficult for veterans to access certain types of care at IHS-funded facilities.[3] Further, it has been reported that many Native American veterans live in very rural areas and have difficulty obtaining transportation to both VA and IHS-funded facilities, or face very long travel times to facilities, which can make it difficult to access care at either type of facility.[4]

In 2010, VA and IHS expanded upon a 2003 memorandum of understanding (MOU), which included provisions to improve Native American veterans' access to VA and IHS facilities and the agencies' coordination of efforts related to the MOU.[5] The 2010 MOU, which aimed to more fully address the core access problems for Native American veterans, includes goals to increase access to health care services for Native American veterans. It also describes strategies intended to achieve this goal. For example, the 2010 MOU includes provisions for expanding outreach through the Tribal Veterans Representative Program, expanding telehealth services, developing payment and reimbursement policies and mechanisms to support care delivered to Native American veterans eligible for care in both systems, and providing training to VA and IHS staff on the agencies' eligibility requirements.[6]

We previously reported on the agencies' coordination of efforts related to the MOU.[7] We examined the extent to which the agencies established mechanisms for MOU implementation and monitoring, the key challenges the agencies faced in implementing the MOU, such as the challenge of coordinating with a large number of unique tribes, and the progress made in overcoming those challenges.

We were asked to report on the extent to which the MOU has increased access to care for Native American veterans. This report examines: (1) the actions that VA and IHS have taken to implement the provisions in the 2010 MOU related to access to care for Native American veterans; and (2) what is known about how access to care for Native American veterans has improved.

To examine the actions that VA and IHS have taken to implement provisions in the 2010 MOU related to access to care for Native American veterans, we collected information from a variety of sources. We reviewed a broad range of documents related to MOU activities, such as quarterly reports that describe MOU-related activities and progress by VA and IHS. We reviewed information and data related to reimbursement by VA to IHS-funded facilities for services provided to Native American veterans. We interviewed agency officials, including leaders of 5 of the 12 work groups that were established to implement the MOU, about actions they have taken to increase access to care, monitor progress, and assess outcomes in improving access. Finally, we conducted site visits to three regions of the country—the Upper Peninsula of Michigan, Northern Arizona, and Alaska—to learn about actions taken by VA and IHS to improve access to care at the local level. The regions were selected to reflect geographic variation, variation in the types of VA and IHS-funded facilities available, and the presence or absence of reimbursement agreements between the VA and IHS-funded facilities. We conducted interviews with: VA and IHS regional officials; VA, IHS, and tribal health facility staff such as administrators, enrollment coordinators, and business office managers; and representatives of tribes. Information obtained through these site visits cannot be generalized to the nationwide Native American veteran population.

To examine what is known about how access to care for Native American veterans has improved, we interviewed Native American veterans and their representatives—such as Tribal Veterans Representatives (TVR)— in 12 interviews during our three site visits.[8] We analyzed this information to determine the extent to which there were positive or negative comments related to changes in access to care for Native American veterans—such as whether interviewees thought that the number of Native American veterans obtaining care at VA or IHS facilities had increased or decreased. We used the following convention to state whether comments were made at most, many, some, or few of these interviews: most—at least one comment in 9 to 11 interviews; many—at least one comment in 5 to 8 interviews; some—at least one comment in 3 to 4 interviews; and few—at least one comment made in 1 to 2 interviews. We also obtained views from an additional 102 representatives of Native American veterans through a Web-based questionnaire.[9] This questionnaire included questions about the extent to which access to care for Native American veterans had changed during the past 3 years. The responses to this questionnaire are not generalizable to the entire population of representatives of Native Americans.

We conducted this performance audit from June 2013 to June 2014 in accordance with generally accepted government auditing standards. Those standards require that we plan and perform the audit to obtain sufficient, appropriate evidence to provide a reasonable basis for our findings and conclusions based on our audit objectives. We believe that the evidence obtained provides a reasonable basis for our findings and conclusions based on our audit objectives.

BACKGROUND

Native American Veterans

While Native American veterans are geographically dispersed throughout the United States, the West and South regions contain the majority of the Native American veteran population, according to Census data. Some Native American veterans are members of the 566 federally recognized tribes that are distinct, independent, political communities that possess certain powers of self-government.[10]

VA and IHS Structure and Benefits

VA is charged with providing health care services to the nation's eligible veterans, and served 6.5 million individual patients in fiscal year 2013. In fiscal year 2013, VA had $56 billion in appropriations available for medical care. VA's health care system includes 21 regional networks—Veterans Integrated Service Networks (VISN)—to which each of VA's 151 medical centers are assigned.[11] The VA medical centers offer a variety of inpatient and outpatient services, ranging from routine examinations to complex surgical procedures. VA's health care system also includes facilities such as community-based outpatient clinics. Eligibility for VA health care is based on several factors, including the veteran's period of active service, discharge status, the presence of service connected disabilities or exposures, income, and other factors such as status as a former prisoner of war. In addition, VA categorizes eligible veterans into eight priority groups, and some veterans may be responsible for co-payments.[12]

IHS was established for the purpose of providing, or arranging for, health care to the approximately 2.2 million eligible Native Americans. IHS's fiscal year 2013 budget was approximately $4.1 billion. While IHS's headquarters is based in the Washington, D.C., area, overall the agency is organized into 12 federally designated geographic service areas that cover all or part of 35 states.[13] IHS provides health care services directly through a system of about 120 facilities that are operated by IHS— including hospitals, health clinics, and health stations. In addition to IHS-operated facilities, some federally recognized tribes choose to operate their own health care facilities—tribal health programs (THPs)—that receive IHS funding. THPs operate the majority of facilities funded by IHS, including 500 facilities, such as hospitals, clinics and health stations. IHS also provides funding to nonprofit, urban Native American organizations through the Urban Indian Health program to provide health care services to Native Americans living in urban areas. To be eligible for IHS health care services, an individual must be a person of Indian descent belonging to the Indian community, as evidenced by such factors as membership, enrollment, residence on tax-exempt land, ownership of restricted property, active participation in tribal affairs, or other relevant factors.[14] In instances where a Native American veteran is eligible for a particular health care service from both VA and IHS, VA is the primary payer.

Memorandum of Understanding

In 2003, VA and IHS signed an MOU to facilitate collaborative efforts in serving Native American veterans eligible for health care in both systems. In 2010, VA and IHS replaced the MOU with an updated MOU, which outlines specific goals and strategies related to increasing access to care for Native American veterans, such as goals to improve outreach and cultural competency, expand services including through telehealth, and develop payment and reimbursement policies. Specifically, the MOU included the following provisions related to access to care:

- providing training for IHS and tribal staff on VA and IHS eligibility requirements to assist them with appropriate referrals for services;
- expanding the TVR program, which uses Native American liaisons to conduct outreach to tribes to assist with veterans' eligibility questions;
- increasing cultural awareness and culturally competent care;
- developing and implementing telehealth services such as telepsychiatry and telepharmacy; and
- increasing the availability of services by developing payment and reimbursement policies and mechanisms.

The MOU provides for a broad range of collaboration between VA and IHS. One goal of the MOU is to bring together strengths and expertise from each agency to improve both the care and services provided by each organization.

VA and IHS designated certain staff to implement the MOU. The two key offices within VA that have been involved in implementing the MOU are the Office of Rural Health (ORH) and the Office of Tribal Government Relations (OTGR). VA created ORH in 2007 to focus on better serving the needs of veterans residing in geographically remote areas through a combination of community-based clinic expansions, increased partnerships with non-VA providers, and increased use of telehealth services.[15] VA established OTGR in 2011 to work to strengthen and enhance partnerships that enhance access to services and benefits for Native American veterans. Within IHS, MOU responsibilities have been delegated to the Chief Medical Officer and staff.

To accomplish the goals set forth in the MOU, VA and IHS created interagency work groups, tasked with implementing and developing strategies to address the goals of the MOU, such as developing payment and reimbursement policies and mechanisms, and developing and implementing new models of care through new technology, including telehealth services.[16] Each work group includes staff from VA and IHS, and, in some cases, tribal representatives. In many cases, work group members volunteered to serve on the work groups. The goals established by each work group align with MOU goals.

One of the work groups, referred to as either the Leadership work group or the Joint Implementation Task Force, is responsible for the oversight and the overall implementation of the MOU, and charged with identifying strategies and plans for accomplishing the goals of the MOU. It includes officials from both agencies, including from the Office of the Secretary of Veterans Affairs, the IHS Chief Medical Officer, and the director of OTGR, and also includes the co-chairs of certain MOU work groups. The agencies defined responsibilities for the Joint Implementation Task Force. Specifically, it is charged with developing implementation plans and procedures for policy-related issues identified by the work groups, creating performance metrics and timelines, collecting quarterly progress reports from the work groups and from other sources such as VA VISN Native American Inventory reports, evaluating progress, identifying priority action items for work groups, and providing an annual report on progress in MOU implementation.[17] According to the MOU 2012 Annual Report, the Joint Implementation Task Force is expected to meet quarterly.

ACTIONS VA AND IHS HAVE TAKEN TO IMPROVE ACCESS TO CARE FOR NATIVE AMERICAN VETERANS FACE IMPLEMENTATION CHALLENGES, AND OVERSIGHT AND ACCOUNTABILITY ARE LACKING

VA and IHS staff have taken actions to improve access to care, including strengthening outreach and enrollment efforts, expanding services offered, increasing efforts to improve cultural competency, and implementing reimbursement agreements. However, according to various stakeholders, these efforts face a variety of implementation challenges, such as a lack of data identifying which Native Americans are veterans, difficulty reaching Native American veterans who live in remote locations, and staff turnover at IHS and THP facilities. In addition, although VA and IHS have identified procedures for collecting information on the various actions taken by VA and IHS facilities to address the goals of the MOU, the agencies lack a defined approach to effectively track and oversee implementation of the MOU.

VA and IHS Have Taken Actions to Improve Access to Care, but Implementation Challenges Limit Their Effectiveness

In four main areas, VA and IHS have taken actions to improve access to care for Native American veterans: (1) outreach and enrollment, (2) expanded services including telehealth, (3) training and improvement in cultural competency, and (4) reimbursement agreements. However, in each of these areas, unresolved challenges prevent these actions from being fully or effectively implemented.

Information Sharing, Training, and Outreach about Enrollment Have Improved, but Sufficient Information to Identify Native Americans and Resources to Help Them Are Lacking

Both agencies have taken actions to improve outreach to Native American veterans and to provide information about enrollment into the VA health system. Specifically, IHS and VA have developed various ways to share information about eligibility and enrollment and VA has conducted a variety of training programs about these topics.

- **Information sharing**: IHS and VA have supported information sharing in a variety of ways with tribes, IHS and THP facilities, and Native American veterans. For example, OTGR published a monthly newsletter focusing on resources available to tribes to promote enrollment in the VA health system. In addition, IHS officials in two of our three site visit areas reported that they organized introductions of VA staff to tribal officials and IHS and THP facility staff, and the VA medical centers in all of these site visit areas reported that they shared information in a variety of ways such as health benefit fairs held at tribal locations, regular conference calls with tribal health officials, and meetings with Native American veterans' organizations. In the Native American Inventory quarterly reports, 20 of 21 VISNs reported one or more information sharing activities, such as making presentations to tribal elders and providing information at tribal health fairs.

- **Training**: VA and IHS conducted a variety of training activities about eligibility and enrollment. VA holds monthly on-line training about the enrollment process that is available for staff at IHS and THP facilities and for representatives of Native American veterans. In partnership with IHS, VA funded multiple regional training events designed to increase knowledge of VA benefits, eligibility criteria, and the enrollment process. Participants in these events included tribal health officials, IHS and THP facility staff, TVRs, and members of Native American veteran military organizations. Facilities in two of our three site visit locations also reported conducting training activities. For example, at one of the sites we visited, IHS provided training to staff at its facilities about VA health benefits and services. In another site visit area, VA officials reported that they recruited and trained over 190 TVRs from 2010 through 2013.

Although VA and IHS have undertaken a variety of outreach efforts, officials from VA, IHS, and THP facilities identified two main ongoing challenges to implementing effective outreach to Native American veterans—the lack of available data to identify eligible Native American veterans and insufficient agency resources to effectively conduct outreach in rural areas.

- **Lack of available data**: VA and IHS headquarters officials, as well as local facility officials in all three of our site visit areas, reported that it is difficult to conduct outreach to Native American veterans because there is limited data identifying who they are. While officials reported that IHS health registration forms include a question about whether the patient is a veteran, officials indicated that patients are not required to report this information. While officials at some IHS and THP facilities with whom we met said they have taken actions to identify veterans in their tribes, others lack such data. An official at one THP facility, for example, said that veteran status data had not been collected from their patients; officials at another THP reported that without a list identifying who is a veteran, it is difficult to conduct outreach and enroll veterans in the VA. Similarly, while VA registration forms include a question about race/ethnicity, VA officials reported that VA facilities have not required veterans to report whether they are Native American, and this limits VA's ability to conduct outreach to Native American veterans.[18]

- **Insufficient resources for effective outreach to very rural areas**:
  VA, IHS and THP officials, and TVRs reported that there are
  insufficient resources—such as outreach volunteers and funding for
  travel—for effective outreach to the remote areas where many Native
  American veterans live. For example, officials at one THP that serves
  an area of approximately 75,000 square miles, including terrain that
  requires travel by boat or plane, reported that they were not aware of
  any TVRs serving their region. Officials at another THP said that
  there was a lack of funding for TVRs to travel to conduct outreach.

More Health Services Are Now Available to Native American Veterans, but Further Progress Has been Slowed by Technical Issues and Delays in Finalizing Service Expansion Agreements

Actions taken by VA and IHS to expand health care services for Native
American veterans include funding for service expansion, a national effort to
increase telehealth connections between VA and IHS, and local efforts to
expand health services through satellite and mobile services and through
telehealth.

- **Funding for service expansion**: Since the MOU was signed, both
  agencies have sponsored funding to support the expansion of health
  services. Specifically, ORH awarded about $1.8 million in funding
  from 2012 through 2014 for five telemental health projects for eligible
  veterans in Native American communities, including the development
  and operation of programs in certain areas of Alaska, Michigan, and
  Oklahoma; and IHS provided financial support to enable the
  expansion of three THP clinics in Alaska, Mississippi, and Oklahoma
  in 2011.
- **National effort to expand telehealth consultation between VA and
  IHS**: Officials from the MOU work group that promotes new
  technology reported that VA and IHS are in the process of completing
  activities designed to improve the connectivity between VA and IHS
  required for live telehealth consultation. VA officials reported that as
  of April 2014, the testing phase was nearing completion. According to
  VA officials, the next step is the development of business plans by
  individual IHS facilities to establish collaborative telehealth programs
  with VA. This work group has also identified opportunities for
  collaboration between the two agencies, specifically on teleretinal
  services for diabetes care.[19]

- **Local efforts to expand services and telehealth**: Data gathered from
  our site visits and our review of the quarterly VISN reports for 2013
  identified a number of local efforts to expand the availability of health
  care services. For example, in one area, officials reported that the
  local VA medical center expanded services to Native American
  veterans in one location by renting space from a THP to provide
  onsite health services to eligible Native American veterans; further, it
  was seeking agreements with two THPs to establish VA-provided
  telehealth services. According to VA and IHS officials at another site
  we visited, the local VA medical center and an IHS facility
  collaborated to establish a VA primary care presence at the IHS
  facility. This VA medical center also initiated similar plans to partner
  with another IHS facility and two THP facilities, established a mobile
  clinic that serves eligible veterans on Native American reservations,
  and added telehealth services to its community based outpatient
  clinics that serve Native American veterans.[20] In the quarterly Native
  American Inventory reports submitted to VA by VISNs, 14 of 21
  VISNs listed one or more efforts to expand telehealth services for
  Native American veterans in their region.

Agency officials and staff at VA, IHS, and THP facilities described three
main challenges that need to be addressed to better ensure the successful
implementation of expansion efforts: (1) the lack of interoperability between
VA and THP computer systems; (2) a lack of technical resources; and (3)
delays in finalizing service expansion agreements.

- **Incompatible systems**: Agency officials said that while VA and IHS
  facilities have been working on connectivity between their VA and
  IHS platforms for telehealth, THPs may use different computer
  systems than IHS; therefore, connectivity between VA and THPs has
  to be tested and explored on a case-by-case basis. This can slow
  collaboration on telehealth services, and tribes that do not use the IHS
  or VA platform would need to obtain the necessary technology. For
  example, in one site visit area, integration of THP and VA telehealth
  has been challenged by differences in technical connectivity and
  information security policies. Since a majority of IHS-funded
  facilities are operated by THPs, the potential for collaboration on
  telehealth services may be limited by the interest and resources
  available from tribes for this purpose.

- **Insufficient technical resources**: According to facility officials in all three site visit areas, the lack of technical resources in some rural locations has hampered the expansion of telehealth or other services such as home-based health. For example, in one area, tribal health officials said that there was no infrastructure to support telehealth services. Also in this area, VA medical center officials said that they explored expanding virtual care through the use of veterans' home computers but found that some veterans lack phone lines or adequate Internet connectivity. In another area, THP facility officials said that there was poor Internet "bandwidth" in their area that reduced the quality of transmission for telehealth
- **Delays in finalizing agreements to expand services**: Agency and facility officials from two of our three site visit areas reported that it can take years to finalize service expansion agreements between VA and IHS or THP facilities, which could limit incentives to pursue such agreements. There were several examples cited in which it took 3 years to finalize service expansion agreements. In one case an official reported that it took 3 years to process an agreement to allow a VA medical center to use a small area in an IHS facility for 2 days per week, in part due to lengthy legal and contracting reviews by VA and IHS. An official in another area reported that it took 3 years and many layers of approval to establish an agreement between the local VA medical center and THP provider to expand optometry services to Native American veterans.

VA and IHS Have Provided Information and Training to Improve Cultural Competency, but Cultural Variation among Tribes and Staff Turnover Limit Its Effectiveness

VA and IHS have distributed informational resources among agency staff and some VA and IHS facilities have provided training to provider staff locally aimed at improving cultural competency. In some cases, the information and training have been targeted at informing VA staff about Native American culture, while in others it has been targeted at informing IHS and THP staff about veterans' issues.[21]

- **Training VA staff about Native American culture**: VA and IHS agency officials said they had promoted informational resources among some agency and health facility staff and conducted training, both of which were designed to improve cultural competency. For example, they have publicized certain informational resources available to VA and IHS staff with respect to Native Americans, including a webinar on Native American behavioral health issues and *A Guide to Build Cultural Awareness* publication.[22] Moreover, at all of our site visit areas, officials reported that staff training and other activities were conducted to improve the cultural competency of care provided to Native American veterans. An official at one VA medical center, for example, reported that they provide a 1-week training program covering Native American culture for providers who work with predominantly Native American patients; this training is followed by tribe-specific educational programs coordinated with a local tribe. Also, IHS-employed, traditional Native healers provided cultural orientations to VA staff. In fiscal year 2013 Native American Inventory quarterly reports submitted by VISNs to VA, 19 of 21 VISNs listed one or more activities related to improving cultural competency related to Native American culture.

- **Training IHS staff about veterans' issues**: VA and IHS agency officials reported that there are a number of training aides to inform IHS staff about veterans' issues, including (1) a video training program for IHS facility officials about PTSD; (2) a webinar distributed by a IHS facility to its staff about PTSD and sexual assault issues in the military; and (3) presentations by VA to THP facility staff about PTSD and traumatic brain injury.

The effectiveness of cultural competency training has been limited by cultural variation across some tribes and by the challenges of high staff turnover in some VA and IHS facilities.

- **Cultural variation**: IHS officials explained that customs and beliefs may vary in important ways across different tribes, and this presents a challenge for providing training that adequately addresses these variations, particularly in cases where VA and IHS facilities serve Native American veterans from multiple tribes. For example, in one site visit area, IHS officials at a facility that primarily served one tribe reported that their native healing practices were different than those of other nearby tribes with regard to the selection of a traditional healer to participate in healing ceremonies. Native American veterans from the tribe reported that if VA and IHS providers did not understand these differences it would make it difficult for their tribal members to obtain culturally competent health care treatment.

- **High staff turnover**: Native American veterans with whom we spoke during our site visits identified high staff turnover as an issue affecting cultural competency. Native American veterans said that the use of temporary staff and the high degree of provider turnover limit the effectiveness of any training in cultural competency, which in turn can diminish the quality of care provided. Without training in cultural competency, provider staff may not be aware of important issues, such as how to effectively communicate with Native American veterans about their health or how to diagnose certain symptoms unique to veterans.

Reimbursement Agreements Are in Place in Many Locations, but Site-Specific Factors and Circumstances Have Limited Establishing Such Agreements in Other Locations

IHS and VA collaborated at the national and local levels to establish a VA-IHS reimbursement agreement that applies to all IHS facilities and to encourage THPs to develop reimbursement agreements with VA. Under such agreements, VA pays IHS and THP facilities for eligible services that they provide to eligible Native American veterans. VA, IHS, and THP officials said that reimbursement agreements may improve access to care because the presence of the agreements may encourage IHS and THP facilities to be more active in outreach and encouraging of enrollment of Native American veterans into VA. This could provide more opportunities for Native American veterans to obtain health care at any type of facility, as well as obtain services they would not otherwise have access to, including services targeted at veterans, such as PTSD counseling and treatment, as well as specialty services unavailable at the IHS or THP facility. The actions taken by the agencies include the development of a national reimbursement agreement between VA and IHS facilities and the development of individual reimbursement agreements between VA and some THPs.

- **National reimbursement agreement covering IHS**: VA and IHS officials explained that together the agencies developed a national reimbursement agreement as well as procedures and systems through which VA payments may be made to IHS facilities. In addition, VA and IHS agency staff worked at the local level to complete implementation plans with each IHS facility and its area VA medical center. Officials reported that all 81 local implementation plans were in place as of July 2013. According to these officials, implementation planning at the local level involved: (1) "get to know you" sessions, in which local VA and IHS officials shared information about what services were provided by their respective facilities; (2) training of IHS staff about VA's eligibility, billing, and enrollment processes; (3) registration of the IHS facility into VA's payment system; and (4) setting up the IHS facility site for billing to VA. Data provided by VA indicates that as of April 8, 2014, VA had paid a total of $3.28 million for services provided to 2,047 Native American veterans at IHS facilities.

- **Reimbursement agreements with THPs**: In addition to a national agreement, VA officials said that VA had established 53 reimbursement agreements with THPs as of May 16, 2014, and conducted additional outreach through tribal letters and events to educate other THPs about the option of establishing these agreements.[23] Data provided by VA indicate that as of April 8, 2014, VA had paid a total of $1.99 million for services provided to 307 Native American veterans at THP facilities.

Challenges cited by officials at VA, IHS, and THP facilities included delays in activating established reimbursement agreements and obstacles to establishing agreements with additional THPs.

- **Delays in starting reimbursement under established agreements**: Not all IHS and THP facilities that are covered under reimbursement agreements have received reimbursement. While there are currently over 130 facilities covered under such agreements, as of April 8, 2014 only 86 had received reimbursement for services provided in fiscal year 2014. According to agency officials, although many agreements are in place, it may take some time before reimbursement will begin at some IHS and THP facilities. Before reimbursement can begin, eligible Native American veterans must be identified as such. However, the previously mentioned challenges of a lack of data that identifies veterans as Native Americans and high staff turnover among IHS facilities have hindered efforts to identify these eligible individuals, according to officials. VA officials said that it takes time to firmly establish the procedures for providing and transmitting complete claims information. For example, some THP facilities do not have the ability to file electronic claims and therefore the process for submitting claims needs to be worked out at each THP, sometimes using paper filing. Officials also said that in some cases the time required to establish reimbursement procedures is extended as a result of staff turnover at THPs. In one case it took a year before the THP's staff consistently provided the necessary information on submitted claims forms.

- **Obstacles to establishing agreements with additional THPs**: Factors such as the time it may take to establish a reimbursement agreement as well as the perceived lack of need for agreements may discourage some THPs from pursuing such agreements. Officials said that while the reimbursement agreement between VA and IHS applies to all IHS facilities, VA's agreements with THPs need to be negotiated individually and are based on each tribal facility's specific circumstances, such as whether it has the accreditation status required by VA to provide care for veterans, and assessment of these unique situations will require time and resources.[24] VA and IHS officials said that some THPs may choose not to invest the time and resources needed to establish agreements for a variety of reasons. For example, the THP may be located near a VA facility and not believe it is necessary to establish such an arrangement. One THP official we interviewed noted that it can take a long time to develop a reimbursement agreement with VA. THP officials cited a range of issues that need to be worked out in these agreements, such as the reimbursement rate, requirements for provider credentialing and privileging, and whether electronic health records would be exchanged. VA has created a template for agreements with THPs which addresses these issues and may expedite the process of finalizing agreements. However, VA officials noted that THPs may propose changes to the template language, and each agreement requires a legal review and a contracting officer's review and signature. VA may have disincentives to sign such agreements as well. For example, VA officials at one facility reported the concern that pursuing a reimbursement agreement with area THPs could divert funds from VA facilities if Native American veterans shifted from using VA services to using THP services.

VA and IHS Lack a Defined Approach for Effectively Implementing and Overseeing the MOU

VA and IHS lack a defined approach for effectively implementing and overseeing the MOU, and we identified three main contributing factors. First, oversight of the MOU's implementation is inconsistent and, in 2013, the officials tasked with this oversight did not meet and did not systematically evaluate the progress of MOU implementation. Second, according to agency officials, no formal policies or guidance have been developed that outline the procedures to implement the MOU, which limits the agencies' ability to hold individuals accountable for its implementation. Third, leadership in VA and IHS have not made MOU implementation a priority, which threatens the ability of the two agencies to move forward in implementing the MOU. Without consistent oversight, formal guidance on responsibilities for MOU implementation, and the prioritization of MOU implementation, leadership in VA and IHS do not have reasonable assurance that the objectives of the MOU related to access to care are being addressed.

Implementation and Oversight Are Inconsistent

Standards for Internal Control in the Federal Government require that the agency's organizational structure define key areas of authority and responsibility, and also that appropriate and clear internal reporting relationships be established.[25] The standards further require top-level reviews of actual performance to track achievements and compare goals and objectives, as well as the assessment of the quality of performance over time to ensure that actions are promptly taken in response to findings or recommendations. They also specify that it is important not only to establish, but also to review, performance measures to ensure they are working as intended. Furthermore, our prior work on interagency collaborations found that collaborating agencies should work together to define and agree on respective roles and responsibilities, including how the efforts will be led.[26] This work also found that federal agencies working together need to create the means to monitor and evaluate efforts to identify areas for improvement.[27]

In implementing the MOU, VA and IHS have not complied with these standards or good practices. For example,

- While the Joint Implementation Task Force held meetings in 2011 and 2012, the full Joint Implementation Task Force has not met since 2012 according to several agency officials, and it was the understanding of one agency official that this group was on a hiatus. Another official with a key role on the Joint Implementation Task Force reported being unaware of who actually led this task force. Another official with a key role on the Joint Implementation Task Force reported that while some of its members met in 2013 to work on implementing the national VA/IHS reimbursement agreement, these meetings did not focus on MOU oversight.
- As of April 2014, officials responsible for leading the Joint Implementation Task Force told us that they had not systematically reviewed or analyzed information in the work group or Native American Inventory quarterly reports for fiscal year 2013, although officials in VA said they had reviewed selected reports for specific purposes, such as learning what types of training were being provided by VISNs. However, the leaders of the Joint Implementation Task Force did not comprehensively track the information provided and therefore did not provide oversight to identify priority action items for work groups or possible obstacles to achieving the goals of the MOU.[28]
- As of fiscal year 2013, the Joint Implementation Task Force has not systematically identified strategies and plans for accomplishing tasks related to the MOU moving forward or addressed challenges or implemented best practices.
- Furthermore, although work groups were tasked with reporting MOU-related activities each quarter, only 28 of the 44 work group quarterly reports due for fiscal year 2013 (64 percent) were submitted. Members of one of the five work groups with whom we spoke reported that they no longer held work group meetings regularly.

Based on our assessment, these problems occurred in 2013 because VA and IHS leaders were not holding themselves or others accountable for their role in implementing the MOU. Without reviewing the quarterly work group reports, and ensuring that all required reports are submitted, VA and IHS leaders do not have reasonable assurance that the objectives of the MOU related to access to care are being addressed. In addition, they may be unaware of challenges and obstacles that VISNs, IHS and THP facilities, and work groups are encountering.

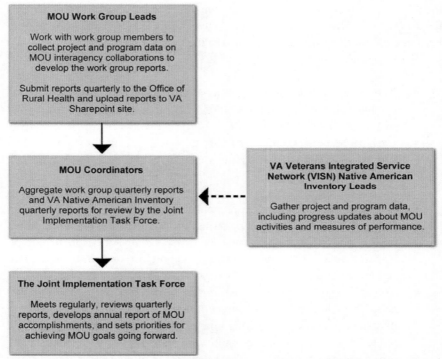

Source: GAO interpretation of Office of Rural Health December 2012 training slides|
    GAO-14-489.

Figure 1. Procedures Outlined in 2012 Training Slides for Tracking and Overseeing
Actions Taken to Achieve the Goals of the Memorandum of Understanding between
the Department of Veterans Affairs (VA) and the Indian Health Service (IHS).

Written Policies and Guidance Are Lacking

While VA and IHS have informal procedures to track and oversee actions
taken under the MOU, the agencies have not developed written policies and
guidelines governing implementation of the MOU. Our prior work on
interagency collaborations found that agencies that articulate agreements—in
areas such as leadership, roles and responsibilities and accountability—in
formal documents can strengthen their commitment to working
collaboratively.[29] According to VA and IHS agency officials, the only
documentation outlining the procedures to report VA and IHS progress in
implementing the MOU is contained in a set of training slides used in a
December 2012 staff training session. Based on the information presented in

the slides, the procedures are generally consistent with *Standards for Internal Control in the Federal Government*.[30] (See figure 1 for a diagram of our interpretation of the procedures outlined in the training slides).

For example:

- The slides include an organizational chart and other information that establish clear reporting relationships and assign key roles and responsibilities to agency staff.
- Each MOU work group is required to collect information and develop a quarterly report detailing the types of activities it has conducted related to MOU objectives, including the objectives aimed at taking actions to improve access to care.[31]
- The MOU coordinators are responsible for providing assistance and training to work groups, aggregating information from the work group reports and other sources such as VA's Native American Inventory Reports, and submitting a quarterly report for review by the Joint Implementation Task Force.[32]
- The Joint Implementation Task Force, made up of officials from VA and IHS including leaders from certain work groups, is responsible for oversight, including reviewing quarterly reports that are submitted by the MOU coordinators, and identifying plans for accomplishing MOU goals going forward.[33] These slides stipulate that the Joint Implementation Task Force should hold regular meetings to review progress and set priorities.

However, VA and IHS officials said that these training slides are not binding because they have not been formalized in written policy or guidance, including establishing clearly defined roles and responsibilities. Without formal written policy or guidance to govern the implementation of the MOU, VA and IHS have little basis to hold those responsible for implementing the MOU accountable for effectively managing the implementation process.

Prioritization of MOU Implementation Is Lacking

VA and IHS leaders have not made MOU implementation a priority, which threatens the ability of the two agencies to move forward in implementing the MOU as it relates to access to care. This is demonstrated in a number of ways. First, according to officials, the Joint Implementation Task Force has not created any written policy or guidance that specifically defines roles and responsibilities for agency staff under the MOU. Moreover, key members of the Joint Implementation Task Force attributed their lack of tracking and oversight of the MOU activities in part to their perception that other work-related responsibilities had a higher priority than some of their MOU related responsibilities. The leaders of the Joint Implementation Task Force from both agencies reported that MOU responsibilities were not their top priority, and that resource constraints have affected their ability to focus attention on oversight of MOU implementation. For example, officials from ORH reported that, while it is the lead office within VA responsible for MOU-related activities, it is also responsible for many other initiatives. The office experienced staff turnover in 2012 and 2013, replacing 4 of its 11 staff members, including members of the leadership team. As a result, current leadership and some staff have only been in their current positions since April 2013 or later and have not had time to fully focus on MOU implementation and oversight. Similarly, an IHS official stated that IHS has limited resources, that agency staff are stretched in order to complete their primary responsibilities, and that activities related to the MOU are a part of their additional responsibilities.[34]

VA and IHS officials reported that they have plans to examine efforts to implement the MOU by looking at the effectiveness of the work group structure.[35] Specifically, VA and IHS have entered into an agreement to have VA's National Center for Organization Development undertake an assessment of the views of work group members about their experience and about whether they think the goals of the MOU are being met. The assessment is scheduled to be completed by May 2014 and, according to officials, will be used to identify best practices for improved efficiency and effectiveness, or the need for adjustments to organizational structure or processes. It is unclear at this point, however, whether this study will fully address the implementation and oversight shortcomings we have noted and whether it will spur greater focus on the leadership required to effectively implement the MOU.

NATIVE AMERICAN VETERANS AND THEIR REPRESENTATIVES REPORTED MIXED VIEWS ON WHETHER ACCESS TO CARE HAS IMPROVED

Although the majority of Native American veterans and their representatives we contacted reported that they thought access to care for Native American veterans had improved over the past 3 years, a number of others said either that they did not believe that access to care had improved during that time or they did not know whether it had. In addition, there were mixed perceptions about the degree to which VA and IHS-funded facilities had made improvements in providing care that was culturally competent with regard to the needs of Native Americans or veterans.

Most Native American veteran representatives that we contacted via questionnaire perceived that there had been improvements in access to care, such as increases in the number of Native American veterans being enrolled in the VA health system and getting health care services. However, others did not see that any gains had been made or did not know. For example, Native American veteran representatives that we contacted provided the following responses to our web-based questionnaire when asked about whether there has been a change in the number of Native American veterans enrolled in the VA:[36]

- Of the 102 representatives, 63 said they thought enrollment had increased, 11 said enrollment had remained the same, 5 said that enrollment had declined, and 23 said they did not know whether enrollment had changed.
- Of the 102 representatives, 53 reported that in the last 3 years there had been an increase in the number of Native American veterans accessing health care at a VA, IHS, or THP facility. However, 12 felt that there had been no change and 36 reported that they didn't know. Of the 53 respondents who reported that there had been an increase in access, 41 reported that access had improved at VA facilities, 25 reported that access had improved at IHS-run facilities, and 24 reported that access had improved at THPs.[37]

Native American veterans and their representatives we interviewed reported similar opinions about whether there had been improvements to access to care. Specifically, most of the 12 interviews we conducted with veterans or their representatives included one or more comments indicating that access to health care had improved.[38] Examples of comments indicating that access had improved included the statements "the area VA liaison had played a big part in increasing [health care] use and enrollment," and "as a result of the assistance provided by TVRs to Native [American] veterans, they have better access to more health care services." However, all of the interviews included one or more comments specifying challenges to access, such as the lack of awareness on the part of Native American veterans about

VA benefits and what services are available to them, lack of transportation, long waiting times, and the lack of enough providers in certain areas such as behavioral health and substance abuse. In addition, some of the interviews included one or more comments by Native American veterans and their representatives that indicated that they thought that access had not improved.

There were also mixed views about the extent to which VA and IHS facilities had made improvements in providing care that was culturally competent with regard to the needs of Native Americans or veterans. For example, Native American veteran representatives who responded to our web-based questionnaire reported the following when asked whether they thought there had been changes in culturally competent care for Native American veterans at different types of facilities:

- Of 102 representatives, 38 said care at VA facilities had generally improved with respect to its cultural competency, 28 said there had been no change, 9 said it had declined, and 26 said they did not know if there had been improvements;
- Of 102 representatives, 36 said care at IHS-run facilities had generally improved with respect to its cultural competency, 25 said there had been no change, 9 said it had declined, and 32 said they did not know; and for THPs, 37 said care at THPs had generally improved with respect to its cultural competency, 25 said there had been no change, 8 said it had declined, and 32 said they did not know.

In many of the 12 site visit interviews we conducted, Native American veterans made one or more comments that care was not culturally competent. For example, in one interview a Native American veteran said that the local VA providers did not understand the cultural needs of his tribe. In another interview, Native American veterans and their representatives said that veterans have significant issues around PTSD and domestic and sexual violence, but that the local IHS health facility was not addressing these issues. At the same time, many of the 12 site visit interviews we conducted also included one or more positive comments about cultural competency. One noted that there had been an increase in the provision of culturally competent care provided by VA because VA had hired a Native American to help with outreach, and another noted that care from their tribal clinic was culturally competent with respect to veterans' needs in part because the facility had a specialist providing wound care who had experience working with veterans.

CONCLUSION

Native American veterans have historically faced many issues in accessing health care and to their credit, both VA and IHS have taken actions under the 2010 memorandum of understanding to improve access to care for Native American veterans. However, significant unresolved challenges still remain that the agencies need to address. Moreover, many Native American veterans and their representatives we contacted believed that the agencies need to build upon actions already taken to improve access for Native American veterans. Addressing access challenges and further improving the overall access to care for Native American veterans is hampered by ineffective oversight and the lack of accountability and prioritization of MOU-related responsibilities among those tasked with implementing the MOU. Written policies, procedures, and guidelines have not been developed to lay out roles and responsibilities, methods for collecting and disseminating information about MOU implementation activities, oversight mechanisms, and the process for assessing progress and developing strategies going forward. Absent clear, binding policies and guidance, oversight and accountability have waned and staff have not assessed progress, addressed barriers, or set priorities for how to accomplish the MOU goals going forward. The lack of oversight also makes it difficult for VA and IHS to know how well MOU activities are being carried out, to identify potential best practices for nationwide implementation, or to address existing or future challenges and strategies. Ultimately, access to VA and IHS facilities could be negatively affected and further progress in improving access compromised.

RECOMMENDATION FOR EXECUTIVE ACTION

To improve access to care for Native American veterans through MOU implementation, we recommend that the Acting Secretary of Veterans Affairs and the Secretary of Health and Human Services take the following action:

Establish written policy or guidance designating specific roles and responsibilities for agency staff to hold leadership accountable and improve implementation and oversight of the MOU. In developing written policies and guidelines, strong consideration should be given to the guidance embodied in the training slides from December 2012, including the following:

- Develop an organizational chart clearly outlining the VA and IHS MOU structure and detailing agency staff roles and responsibilities.
- Require that regularly scheduled meetings be held by the Joint Implementation Task Force or other groups charged with the oversight of MOU implementation.
- Ensure that VISNs and the MOU work groups submit reports to VA and IHS quarterly, as well as ensure that the groups charged with the oversight of MOU implementation complete reviews and analyses of the information collected to assess MOU progress and address any deficiencies.
- Ensure that the Joint Implementation Task Force, or other groups charged with oversight of MOU implementation, identifies strategies and plans for accomplishing tasks related to the MOU to implement best practices and address challenges.

AGENCY COMMENTS

We provided draft copies of this report to VA and HHS for review. Both agencies concurred with our recommendation and in their comments on the draft described the plans for implementing the recommendation. Most noteworthy, they reported that the agencies will develop an organizational chart outlining VA and IHS MOU structure and agency roles and responsibilities, hold quarterly leadership meetings to provide oversight and guide the direction of MOU implementation efforts, and adopt and disseminate a Standard Operating Procedure outlining data reporting and submission requirements for work groups responsible for MOU implementation. VA also provided technical comments, which were incorporated in the draft as appropriate.

Randall B. Williamson
Director, Health Care

End Notes

[1] For the purposes of our report, the term Native American includes both American Indians and Alaska Natives.

According to the U.S. Census Bureau, in 2012 approximately 162,000 individuals identified themselves as Native American veterans. This includes only individuals who identified as American Indian or Alaska Native alone and not in combination with another racial group. Therefore, it underestimates the number of Native American veterans.

[2] IHS-funded facilities include both facilities that are operated by the IHS and tribal health program (THP) facilities that are funded by IHS, but operated by the tribes.

Hearing on VA and Indian Health Service Cooperation: Hearing Before the Committee on Veterans' Affairs, United States Senate, 111th Cong (November 5, 2009).

[3] For the purposes of this report, we define cultural competency in terms of health care services as the respect and response to the health beliefs, practices, and cultural and linguistic needs of diverse patients. It refers to Native American traditions, beliefs and practices, but also to clinical care needs of veterans.

Hearing on VA and Indian Health Service Cooperation: Hearing Before the Committee on Veterans' Affairs, United States Senate, 111th Cong. (November 5, 2009).

[4] See *Broken Promises: Evaluating the Native American Health Care System*, U.S. Commission on Civil Rights (September 2004): 77-80; and *Frequently Asked Questions about the Native Domain*, Veterans Health Administration: Office of Rural Health, http://www.ruralhealth.va.gov/native/faqs.asp, accessed June 2, 2014.

[5] The MOU indicates that improvements in access to care may be achieved through an increase in the amount and types of services available to Native American veterans and the use of more geographically accessible services (e.g., mobile services, telehealth, and sharing of staff.) In some cases, enrollment in the VA may give Native American veterans access to services not readily available at certain IHS or Tribal Health Program (THP) facilities.

[6] Telehealth includes telemedicine, which is the use of medical information exchanged from one site to another via electronic communications (such as video or e-mail) to improve a patient's clinical health status through, for example, provision of health care services or clinical monitoring. Telehealth can include telemental health—the provision of mental health services to patients living in remote locations or otherwise underserved areas.

[7] See GAO, *VA and IHS: Further Action Needed to Collaborate on Providing Health Care to Native American Veterans*, GAO-13-354 (Washington, D.C.: Apr. 26, 2013).

[8] TVRs conduct outreach to educate Native American veterans about the availability of veterans' benefits and the process for enrolling for these benefits. They are often volunteers and may receive training from VA. In addition to TVRs, other staff who assist Native American veterans are Tribal Outreach Workers, Veterans Service Officers, and Tribal Veterans Service Officers. In this report we will refer to all such types of individuals as representatives of Native American veterans.

[9] We obtained contact information for these individuals from a variety of sources including VA, national veterans service organizations, and state offices of veterans' affairs.

[10] Federally recognized tribes have government-to-government relationships with the United States, and are eligible for certain funding and services provided by the United States because of their status as Indians.

In addition, some Native American veterans are members of the more than 400 Native American groups that are not recognized by the federal government. Veterans who are members of these Native American groups may be eligible for VA benefits, but are not generally eligible for IHS benefits. For more information on federal funding for non-federally recognized tribes, see GAO, *Indian Issues: Federal Funding for Non-Federally Recognized Tribes*, GAO-12-348, (Washington, D.C.: Apr. 12, 2012).

[11] Each VA medical center is assigned to a single VISN.

[12] See 38 U.S.C. § 1705; 38 C.F.R. § 17.36(b). To manage its provision of health care services for eligible veterans, VA operates a system of annual patient enrollment in accordance with eight priorities listed in statute. VA may change which priority groups and sub-groups of veterans are eligible for enrollment by amending the applicable regulation. See 38 C.F.R. § 17.36(c).

[13] The 12 IHS service areas are Alaska, Albuquerque, Bemidji, Billings, California, Great Plains, Nashville, Navajo, Oklahoma City, Phoenix, Portland, and Tucson.

[14] See 42 C.F.R. § 136.12.

[15] ORH is located in the Office of the Assistant Deputy Undersecretary for Policy and Planning of the Veterans Health Administration.

[16] The work groups are: Services and Benefits; Coordination of Care; Health Information Technology; New Technologies; System Level; Payment and Reimbursement; Sharing of Care Process, Programs and Services; Cultural Competency and Awareness; Training and Recruitment; Emergency and Disaster Preparedness; Alaska; and Leadership.

[17] Work group reports are submitted on a quarterly basis. They are intended to collect project and program data on MOU interagency collaborations. The Native American Inventory Reports are submitted by VISNs to VA on a quarterly basis. They are intended to provide information about projects and activities conducted by VA and IHS staff in each VISN area to support Native American veterans.

[18] A VA official told us that historically, VA has not required the reporting of race and ethnicity data in part because it has been accused of using race and ethnicity to bias the disability claim/adjudication process. As a result, Native American veterans may choose not to report their ethnicity because they believe that it will bias how they are treated. Race/ethnicity data may be recorded in the VA medical record as little as 50 percent of the time.

[19] Diabetes is the leading cause of adult vision loss in the United States. Digital retinal imaging with remote image interpretation (teleretinal imaging) assists in providing eye care to patients with diabetes.

[20] The degree to which there is a need to expand VA services to IHS and THP facilities may vary by region depending on the number, size, and geographic distribution of local tribes, and also by the range of services already available at the area's IHS and THP facilities.

[21] Cultural competency training may address the spiritual beliefs and traditional healing practices of Native Americans, including those related to beliefs about warfare as well as the nature of disease and appropriate ways to communicate about disease. Cultural competency training may also address the special issues faced by some veterans, such as PTSD, domestic violence, and combat-related poisoning.

[22] Department of Health and Human Services, Substance Abuse and Mental Health Services Administration, *CultureCard: A Guide to Build Cultural Awareness – American Indian and Alaska Native*, SMA 08-4354 (January 2009).

[23] The earliest THP reimbursement agreements were completed in Alaska where, as of August 2012 there were 26 agreements that collectively covered nearly all THPs in that state. Unlike agreements in other parts of the United States, these reimbursement agreements also provide Alaska THPs with payment for eligible services for eligible veterans who are not Native American. This arrangement is meant to address the fact that VA has a limited number of health facilities in the state.

[24] Under the Indian Self-Determination and Education Assistance Act, as amended, federally recognized Indian tribes can enter into self-determination contracts or self-governance compacts with the Secretary of Health and Human Services to take over the administration of certain IHS programs for Indians. In such cases the VA must work with each tribe individually regarding its specific program. *See* 25 U.S.C. §§ 450f(a), 458aaa-3.

[25] GAO, *Standards for Internal Control in the Federal Government*, GAO/AIMD-00-21.3.1 (Washington, D.C.: Nov. 1999). Internal controls are components of an organization's management that provide reasonable assurance that certain objectives are being met.

[26] GAO, *Results-Oriented Government: Practices That Can Help Enhance and Sustain Collaboration among Federal Agencies*, GAO-06-15 (Washington, D.C.: Oct. 21, 2005).

[27] GAO-06-15.

[28] VA officials told us that they do have plans to review the quarterly reports for the first quarter of 2014.

[29] GAO-06-15.

[30] GAO/AIMD-00-21.3.1.

[31] The slides stipulate that work groups should upload the reports to a centralized, internal VA website. VA developed a quarterly reporting template for the work group reports aligned according to MOU goals. In addition to describing activities conducted, these reports may also note accomplishments or barriers to activities conducted.

[32] The Native American Inventory Reports submitted by VISNs are aligned according to MOU goals. At the same time, VA officials told us that these reports are intended to serve other purposes within VA, in addition to those of the MOU.

[33] The Joint Implementation Task Force is also referred to as the leadership work group, which was established by the 2010 MOU.

[34] The 2013 and 2014 individual performance plans for two key leaders in VA and IHS who are involved with the MOU indicate general expectations relating to the MOU, for example "provide leadership to MOU implementation and report on MOU progress."

[35] This is consistent with our past work on practices that can enhance and sustain collaboration by revisiting and refreshing interagency groups. See GAO, *Managing for Results: Implementation Approaches Used to Enhance Collaboration in Interagency Groups*, GAO-14-220 (Washington, D.C.: Feb. 14, 2014).

[36] The responses to this questionnaire are not generalizable to the entire population of representatives of Native Americans; however, they provide insights about improvements in access to care.

[37] Respondents could report increases at more than one type of facility. Also, the type of facilities available in a respondent's service area may vary. For example, there may be only THP or IHS-run facilities in a service area but not both.

[38] We used the following convention to state whether specific types of comments were made at most, some, or few of these interviews: most—at least one comment in 9 to 11 interviews; many—at least one comment in 5 to 8 interviews; some—at least one comment in 3 to 4 interviews; and few—at least one comment made in 1 to 2 interviews.

In: Native American Veterans' Access ...   ISBN: 978-1-63463-064-1
Editor: Lorrie Hobbs   © 2014 Nova Science Publishers, Inc.

Chapter 3

MEMORANDUM OF UNDERSTANDING BETWEEN THE DEPARTMENT OF VETERANS AFFAIRS (VA) AND INDIAN HEALTH SERVICE (IHS)[*]

Department of Veterans Affairs and Indian Health Service

I. PURPOSE

The purpose of this Memorandum of Understanding (MOU) is to establish coordination, collaboration, and resource-sharing between the Department of Veterans Affairs (VA) and Indian Health Service (HIS) to improve the health status of American Indian and Alaska Native Veterans. The goal of the MOU is to foster an environment that brings together the strengths and expertise of each organization to actively improve the care and services provided by both. The MOU establishes mutual goals and objectives for ongoing collaboration between VA and IHS in support of their respective missions and to establish a common mission of serving our nation's American Indian (AI) and Alaska Native (AN) Veteran. The MOU is intended to provide authority for a broad range of collaboration between the agencies that facilitate development of additional agreements around

---

[*] This is an edited, reformatted and augmented version of a document issued October 1, 2010.

specific activities. It is the intent of this MOU to facilitate collaboration between IHS and VA, and not limit initiatives, projects, or interactions between the agencies in any way. The MOU recognizes the importance of a coordinated and cohesive effort on a national scope, while also acknowledging that the implementation of such efforts requires local adaptation to meet the needs of individual tribes, villages, islands, and communities, as well as local VA. IHS, Tribal, and Urban Indian health programs.

II. AUTHORITY

The Indian Health Care Improvement Act, 25 U.S.C. Sections 1645, 1647; 38 U.S.C. Sections 523(a), 6301-6307, 8153

III. BACKGROUND

The mission of the Indian Health Service, in partnership with American Indian and Alaska Native people, is to raise their physical, mental, social and spiritual health to the highest level. The goal of IHS is to ensure that comprehensive, culturally acceptable personal and public health services are available and accessible to all American Indian and Alaska Native people. The foundation of IHS is to uphold the Federal Government's obligation to promote healthy American Indian and Alaska Native people, communities, and cultures and to honor and protect the inherent sovereign rights of Tribes.

The mission of the Department of Veterans Affairs is to "care for him who shall have borne the battle and his widow and orphan." Those words were spoken by Abraham Lincoln during his second inaugural address and reflect the philosophy and principles that guide VA in everything it does.

IHS and VA enter into this MOU to further their respective missions. This MOU builds upon decades of successful collaboration, as well as the 2003 MOU signed between IHS and VA. This MOU also conforms to the most current legislation. It is the intent of this MOU that, through appropriate coordination, collaboration, and resource sharing, both organizations will achieve greater success in reaching their organizational goals and in more effectively serving as stewards of public resources.

IV. ACTIONS

A. This MOU sets forth 5 mutual goals:
1. Increase access to and improve quality of health care and services to the mutual benefit of both agencies. Effectively leverage the strengths of the VA and IHS at the national and local levels to afford the delivery of optimal clinical care.
2. Promote patient-centered collaboration and facilitate communication among VA, IHS, American Indian and Alaska Native Veterans, Tribal facilities, and Urban Indian Clinics.
3. In consultation with tribes at the regional and local levels, establish effective partnerships and sharing agreements among VA headquarters and facilities, IHS headquarters and IHS, Tribal, and Urban Indian health programs in support of American Indian and Alaska Native Veterans.
4. Ensure that appropriate resources are identified and available to support programs for American Indian and Alaska Native Veterans.
5. Improve health-promotion and disease-prevention services to American Indians and Alaska Natives to address community-based wellness.

B. To further the goals of this MOU, VA and IHS agree to actively collaborate and coordinate:
1. To **increase access** to services and benefits of IHS and VA (including the Veterans Benefits Administration (VBA)) for AI/AN Veterans, by:
    a. Expanding the highly successful Tribal Veterans Representative (TVR) program into the Indian health system, through integration into existing infrastructure.
    b. Providing systematic training for Benefits Coordinators at IHS, Tribal, and Urban programs in eligibility requirements for VBA benefits and priority designations for VA services and tools to assist them with appropriate referrals for benefits and services.
    c. Providing systematic training for appropriate VA staff on IHS services and IHS Contract Health Services (CHS) eligibility and tools to assist them with appropriate referrals for services.

2. To **improve coordination of care,** including co-management, for Al/AN Veterans served by both IHS, Tribal, or Urban Indian health programs and VA by:

   a. Developing and testing of innovative approaches to improve coordination of care and dissemination of best practices.

   b. Establishing standardized mechanisms for access by providers in one system to the electronic health records in the other system for patients receiving care in both systems.

3. To **improve care** through the development of health information technology, including the following:

   a. Sharing of technology

      i. Joint development of applications and technologies.

      ii. Adaptation of applications and technologies developed by one agency to permit use by the other.

      iii. Mechanisms for the exchange of funds to support this adaptation and sharing.

   b. Interoperability of systems to facilitate sharing of information on common patients and populations

   c. The VA and IHS will develop processes to share information regarding planned development of applications and technologies to facilitate this collaboration.

   d. The VA and IHS will develop standard, pre-approved language for inclusion in sharing agreements to support this collaboration.

4. To **enhance access** through the development and implementation of new models of care using new technologies, including:

   a. Tele-health services such as tale-psychiatry and tela-pharmacy.

   b. Services using mobile communication technologies.

   c. Enhanced telecommunications infrastructure to support collaboration in remote areas.

   d. Sharing of training programs and materials supporting these models of care.

   e. Sharing of knowledge gained from testing of new models of care.

5. To **improve efficiency and effectiveness** of both the VA and IHS at a system level through:

    a. Sharing of contracts and purchasing agreements that may be advantageous to both IHS and VA, supported by the development of:

        i. Standard, pre-approved language for inclusion of one party into contracts and sharing agreements developed by the other.

        ii. Processes to share information at an early stage of strategic planning to facilitate inclusion of one party into contracts and sharing agreements developed by the other.

    b. Development of pre-approved templates for agreements to facilitate local, regional, and national collaborations.

    c. Development of standard policies for use when IHS and VA facilities are co-located.

6. To **increase availability of services, in accordance with law,** by the development of payment and reimbursement policies and mechanisms to:

    a. Support care delivered to eligible AI/AN Veterans served at VA and IHS.

    b. Facilitate the sharing and coordination of services, training, contracts, and sharing agreements, sharing of staff, and development of health information technology and improved coordination of care as specified elsewhere in this agreement.

7. To **improve the delivery of care** through active sharing of care process, programs, and services with benefit to those served by both IHS and VA.

    a. Examples of important collaborations currently underway include: the Consolidated Mail Outpatient Pharmacy, Post-Traumatic Stress Disorder, Home-Based Primary Care, and dementia care, but many additional opportunities exist and should be jointly pursued under this agreement. Especially valuable may be services where one party has unique expertise to share with the other, e.g. VA expertise in PTSD treatment and IHS expertise in diabetes management.

    b. To facilitate this sharing, IHS and VA will, in consultation with the Tribes, develop a strategic investment plan to identify high priority services and programs for collaboration and for possible joint investment of resources.

8. To **increase cultural awareness and culturally competent care** for VA and IHS beneficiaries. Recognizing that many cultures are represented in the populations served by IHS, Tribal and Urban Indian health programs and by VA, this will require:
   a. Attention to cultural issues of importance in caring for American Indians and Alaska Native Veterans in the unique systems of care represented by VA and by IHS, Tribal, and Urban Indian health programs.
   b. Attention to cultural issues of importance for the local Tribes and communities served.

9. To **increase capability and improve quality** though training and workforce development, including:
   a. Sharing of educational and training opportunities and the development of joint training initiatives.
   b. Provision of continuing education units (CEUs) and continuing medical education (CMEs) activities at VA training to Indian health staff and at Indian health training to VA staff.
   c. Education of residents, students, preceptors, and staff in IHS, Tribal, Urban and VA settings.
   d. Sharing and exchange of staff for training opportunities.
   e. Sharing of existing on-line and satellite training resources.
   f. Collaboration on development of training opportunities.
   g. Development of processes to share information regarding planned or projected training opportunities to facilitate this collaboration.

10. To **increase access to care** through sharing of staff and enhanced recruitment and retention of professional staff, including:
    a. Sharing of specialty services.
    b. Joint credentialing and privileging of staff.
    c. Joint training initiatives.
    d. Sharing materials and training in the use of Title 38 wage and benefits system.
    e. Joint facility/service planning.
    f. Facilitation of the temporary assignment of Commissioned Officers to the VA
       i. For short-term training and projects.
       ii. For long-term training and service delivery

iii. For deployment through existing rapid deployment force (RDF) programs and other Public Health Service emergency staffing systems to meet the needs of the VA in responding to public health crises of a regional and national nature.

11. To **address emergency, disaster, and pandemic preparedness and response,** including:

   a. Sharing of contingency planning and preparedness efforts, especially with regard to rural and vulnerable populations.

   b. Joint development of materials targeting AII/N Veterans and their families and communities.

   c. Joint exercises and coordination of emergency response.

12. To **accomplish the broad and ambitious goals of this agreement** through the development of a joint Implementation Task Force to identify the strategies and plans for accomplishing the tasks and aims of this agreement, including:

   a. Development of joint workgroups for both short-term and ongoing work necessary to accomplish the aims of this agreement.

   b. Regular meeting of IHS and VA leadership at multiple levels in the organizations to review progress and set priorities.

   c. An annual report of activities accomplished under the auspices of this agreement.

V. OTHER CONSIDERATIONS

A. VA and IHS will comply with all applicable Federal laws and regulations, including those regarding the confidentiality of health information and the release of information to the public. For example, Medical records of IHS and VA patients are Federal records and are subject to some or all of the following laws: the Privacy Act, 5 U.S.C. 552a; the Freedom of Information Act, 5 U.S.C. 552; the Drug Abuse Prevention, Treatment, and Rehabilitation Act, 21 U.S.C. 1101, the Comprehensive Alcohol Abuse and Alcoholism Prevention, Treatment and Rehabilitation Act, 42 U.S.C. 4541, the Health Insurance Portability and Accountability Act of 1996, 42 U.S.C.1301, VA's Confidentiality of

Certain Medical Records, 38 U.S.C. 7332; Confidential Nature of Claims, 38 U.S.C. 5701; Medical Quality Assurance Records Confidentiality, 38 U.S.C. 5705, and Federal regulations promulgated to implement those acts.

B. Care rendered under this MOU will not be part of a study, research grant, or other test without the written approval of both IHS and VA, subject to all appropriate IHS and VA research protocols.

C. VA and IHS agree to cooperate fully with each other in any investigations, negotiations, settlements or defense in the event of a notice of claim, complaint, or suit relating to care rendered under this MOU.

D. No services under this MOU will result in any reduction in the range of services, quality of care or established priorities for care provided to the Veteran population or IHS service population. Rather the intent of this MOU is to increase the efficiency of services rendered by VA and IHS.

E. VA will provide IHS employees with access to VA automated patient records maintained on VA computer systems to the extent permitted by applicable Federal confidentiality and security laws and policies. Additionally, IHS will likewise provide VA employees access to Veteran IHS records to the same extent permitted by applicable Federal confidentiality and security laws and policies.

F. Both parties to this MOU are Federal agencies and their employees are covered by the Federal Tort Claims Act, 28 U.S.C §§1346(b), 2671-2680, in the event of an allegation of negligence. It is agreed that any and all claims of negligence attributable to actions taken pursuant to this MOU will be submitted to legal counsel for both parties for investigation and resolution.

G. This MOU replaces and supersedes the MOU signed by the Department of Veterans Affairs and the Department of Health and Human Services on February 25, 2003.

VI. TERMINATION

This MOU can be terminated by either party upon issuance of written notice to the other party not less than 30 days before the proposed termination date. The 30 days notice may be waived by mutual written consent of both parties involved in the MOU.

VII. EFFECTIVE PERIOD

VA and IHS will review the MOU annually to determine whether terms and provisions are appropriate and current.

VIII. SEVERABILITY

If any term or condition of this MOU becomes invalid or unenforceable, such term or provision shall in no way affect the validity or enforceability of any other term or provision contained herein.

For the Department of Veterans Affairs
Robert A. Petzel
Under Secretary for Health

For the Department of and Health and Human Services

Yvette Roubideaux
Indian Health Service Director

INDEX